CURRICULUM

HSP Science

D1245626

Assessment Guide
Grade 4

Harcourt
SCHOOL PUBLISHERS

Visit *The Learning Site!*
www.harcourtschool.com

CUR
5
H
4
2009
AG

Contents

Unit A: A World of Living Things

Unit B: Looking at Ecosystems

Overview

In *HSP Science*, the assessment program, like the instruction, is student-oriented. By allowing all learners to show what they know and can do, the program provides you with ongoing information about each student's understanding of science. Equally important, the assessment program offers ample opportunity for students to evaluate their own growth.

The assessment program in *HSP Science* offers the assessment options shown in the chart below. The various options reveal the multidimensional aspect of the program.

Assessment Options		
Formal Assessment • Chapter Review and Test Preparation **SE** • Chapter Test **AG** • Unit Test **AG**	**Ongoing Assessment** • Assess Prior Knowledge— Chapter Opener **TE** • Daily Inquiry Transparencies • Teacher Edition questions **throughout** • Focus Skill questions **throughout SE** • Differentiated Instruction **throughout TE** • Lesson Review **SE** • Observation Checklist **AG**	**Performance Assessment** • Long-Option **AG** • Short-Option **TE**
Standardized Test Preparation • Lesson Review **SE**		**Student Self-Assessment** • Investigate Self-Assessment **Lab Manual** • Self-Assessment **AG**
Online Assessment • Online chapter and unit tests with automatic scoring • Item bank from which to build tests		**Portfolio Assessment** • Using Portfolio Assessment **AG** • Suggested work samples **TE**

(Key: SE = Student Edition; TE = Teacher Edition; AG = Assessment Guide)

Assessment Components

Formal Assessment

To help you reinforce and assess mastery of chapter objectives, *HSP Science* includes both reviews and tests. You will find the Chapter Review and Test Preparation in the student book and the Chapter Test and Unit Test in this **Assessment Guide**. Answers to all assessments, including sample responses to constructed-response items, are provided.

Standardized Test Preparation

Large-scale assessment of science literacy has been mandated by the *No Child Left Behind Act (NCLB)*, the 2001 reauthorization of the Elementary and Secondary Education Act. To help prepare students for district- or state-mandated assessments, *HSP Science* includes items that reflect the format of standardized tests. These items can be found in each Lesson Review and Chapter Review and Test Prep in the **Student Edition.**

Online Assessment

The ability to deliver tests online provides the teacher with increased flexibility in managing classroom assessment. The Chapter Tests and Unit Tests that appear in this **Assessment Guide** can be delivered online. In addition, *Online Assessment* allows you to assemble custom tests from a bank of multiple-choice, short-response, and extended-response items. Multiple-choice items are scored automatically, and a user-friendly interface allows teachers to enter scores for short- and extended-response items. You can also build tests according to state standards. For more information, visit **www.hspscience.com.**

Ongoing Assessment

HSP Science supports ongoing assessment in several ways. Within each lesson in the **Student Edition**, there is a Focus Skill question at the end of each section to help you assess students' immediate recall of information. At the end of each lesson is a Lesson Review to help you evaluate how well students grasped the concepts taught.

The **Teacher Edition** offers a number of informal assessment tools. By using the Assess Prior Knowledge that accompanies each chapter opener, you can gauge students' foundational knowledge. Daily Inquiry Transparencies are designed to reinforce and evaluate students' use of inquiry skills. Questions that address a variety of dimensions—including critical thinking skills, inquiry skills, and use of reading strategies—are strategically placed throughout each lesson. Additional material for reviewing the lesson is provided in **Reading Support and Homework.** Located in this **Assessment Guide** is yet another tool, the Observation Checklist (p. AGxv), on which you can record noteworthy classroom observations.

Performance Assessment

Performance tasks provide evidence of students' ability to use science inquiry skills and critical thinking skills to complete an authentic task. A brief performance task is included as part of the information in the **Teacher Edition** that accompanies each chapter review. A more comprehensive performance task follows each Chapter Test in this **Assessment Guide.** Each includes teacher directions and a scoring rubric. Also in this booklet, you will find the Experiment/Project Evaluation Checklist (p. AGxviii) for evaluating unit inquiries and projects.

Student Self-Assessment

Students should be challenged to reflect on their work and to monitor and control their own learning. Various checklists are provided for this purpose. An Investigate Self-Assessment accompanies each Investigate in the **Lab Manual** in Grades 3–6. This simple checklist allows students to evaluate their performance, using criteria specific to each activity. Two checklists are located in this **Assessment Guide.** One is the Self-Assessment—Read and Learn (p. AGxvii), which helps students reflect on instruction in a particular lesson or chapter. The other is the Experiment/Project Summary Sheet (p. AGxix), on which students describe and evaluate their own science projects and experiments.

Portfolio Assessment

In *HSP Science*, students may create their own portfolios. The portfolio contains self-selected work samples that the student feels represent increased science literacy. The portfolio may also contain a few required or teacher-selected papers. Support materials are included in this **Assessment Guide** (pp. AGxx–AGxxiv) to assist you and your students in developing portfolios.

Formal Assessment

Formal assessment is an essential part of any comprehensive assessment program because it provides an objective measure of student achievement. This traditional form of assessment typically consists of reviews and tests that assess how well students understand, communicate, and apply what they have learned.

Formal Assessment in *HSP Science*

Formal assessment in *HSP Science* includes the following tools: Chapter Review and Test Preparation in the **Student Edition** and Chapter and Unit Assessments in this **Assessment Guide.** The purpose of the review is to assess and reinforce not only chapter concepts and inquiry skills but also students' test-taking skills. The purpose of the Chapter and Unit Assessments is, as with other formal assessments, to provide an objective measure of student performance. Answers to chapter reviews, including sample responses to constructed-response items, are located in the **Teacher Edition**, while answers to chapter and unit tests are located in the Answer Key in this booklet.

The chapter and unit tests that appear in this **Assessment Guide** may be delivered electronically by using *Online Assessment*. For more information, visit **www.hspscience.com.**

Types of Review and Test Items

Students can be overwhelmed by the amount of information on a test and uneasy about how to answer different types of test questions. The Chapter Review and Test Preparation is designed to help familiarize students with the various item formats they may encounter: *multiple-choice items* (with a question stem; graph, table, map, diagram, model, or picture; or using qualifiers such as *not*, *least*, and so on), *constructed-response items* (which, depending on grade level, require the student to write a short or an extended answer), and *context-dependent sets*, in which the student is asked to respond to related items.

Test-Taking Tips

Understandably, students often experience test-related anxiety. Teaching students to apply a number of general test-taking strategies may bolster their confidence and result in improved student performance on formal assessment. As students take a test, they should

- scan the entire test first before answering any questions.
- read the directions slowly and carefully before beginning a section.
- begin with the easiest questions or most familiar material.
- read the question and all answer options before selecting an answer.
- watch out for key words such as *not*, *least*, *best*, *most,* and so on.
- carefully analyze graphs, tables, diagrams, and pictures that accompany items.
- double-check answers to catch and correct errors.
- erase all mistakes completely and write corrections neatly.

Test Preparation

Students perform better on formal assessments when they are well prepared for the testing situation. Here are some things you can do before a test to help your students do their best work.

- Explain the nature of the test to students.
- Suggest that they review the questions at the end of the lessons and the chapter.
- Remind students to get a good night's sleep before the test.
- Discuss why they should eat a balanced meal beforehand.
- Encourage students to relax while they take the test.

Performance Assessment

Teachers today have come to realize that the multiple-choice format of traditional tests, while useful and efficient, cannot provide a complete picture of students' growth in science. Standardized multiple-choice tests cannot fully reveal how students *think and do things*—an essential aspect of science literacy. Performance assessment can provide this missing information and help balance your assessment program. Well-constructed performance assessments provide a window through which teachers may view students' thought processes.

An important feature of performance assessment is that it involves a hands-on activity in which students solve a situational problem. Students often find performance assessment more enjoyable than traditional paper-and-pencil tests. Another advantage is that it models good instruction: students are assessed as they learn and learn as they are assessed.

Performance Assessment in *HSP Science*

Performance tasks can be found in two locations in *HSP Science*. In the **Teacher Edition**, a brief performance task is part of the information that accompanies each chapter review. In this **Assessment Guide**, a more comprehensive task follows each chapter test. Both types of performance tasks will provide insights into students' ability to apply key science inquiry skills and concepts taught in the chapter. You may use the Experiment/Project Evaluation Checklist (p. AGxviii) to evaluate student performance on these tasks.

Administering Performance Tasks

Unlike traditional assessment tools, performance assessment does not provide standardized directions for its administration or impose specific time limits on students, although a suggested time frame is offered as a guideline. The suggestions that follow may help you define your role in this assessment.

- *Be prepared.*
  A few days before students begin the task, read the Teacher's Directions and gather the materials needed.

- *Be clear.*
  Explain the directions for the task; rephrase them as needed. Also, explain how students' performance will be evaluated. Show students the rubric you plan to use, and explain the performance indicators in language your students understand.

- **Be encouraging.**
  Your role in administering the assessments should be that of a coach—motivating, guiding, and encouraging students to produce their best work.

- **Be supportive.**
  You may assist students who need help. The amount of assistance needed will depend on the needs and abilities of individual students.

- **Be flexible.**
  Not all students need to proceed through the performance task at the same rate and in the same manner. Allow students adequate time to do their best work.

- **Involve students in evaluation.**
  Invite students to join you as partners in the evaluation process, particularly in development or modification of the rubric.

Rubrics for Assessing Performance

A well-written rubric can help you score students' work accurately and fairly. Moreover, before students begin a task, it gives them a better idea of what qualities their work should exhibit.

Each performance task in the program has its own rubric. The rubric lists performance indicators, which are brief statements of what to look for in assessing the skills and understandings that the task addresses. A sample rubric for a task in this **Assessment Guide** follows.

Scoring Rubric

Performance Indicators

_____ Assembles the kite successfully.

_____ Carries out the experiment daily.

_____ Records results accurately.

_____ Makes an accurate chart and uses it to report the strength of wind observed each day.

Observations and Rubric Score

| 3 | 2 | 1 | 0 |

Scoring a Performance Task

The scoring system used for performance tasks in this **Assessment Guide** is a 4-point scale that is compatible with those used by many state assessment programs. You may wish to modify the rubrics as a 3- or 5-point scale. To determine a student's score on a performance task, review the indicators checked on the rubric and then select the score that best represents the student's overall performance on the task.

4-Point Scale			
Excellent Achievement	Adequate Achievement	Limited Achievement	Little or No Achievement
3	2	I	0

How to Convert a Rubric Score into a Grade

If, for grading purposes, you want to record a letter or numerical grade rather than a holistic score for the student's performance on a task, you can use the following conversion table:

Holistic Score	Letter Grade	Numerical Grade
3	A	90–100
2	B	80–89
I	C	70–79
0	D–F	69 or below

Developing Your Own Rubric

From time to time, you may want to either develop your own rubric or work together with your students to create one. Research has shown that significantly improved performance can result from student participation in the construction of rubrics.

Developing a rubric for a performance task involves three basic steps: (1) Identify the inquiry skills that are taught in the chapter and that students must perform to complete the task successfully, and identify what understanding of content is also required. (2) Determine which skills and understandings are involved in each step. (3) Decide what you will look for to confirm that the student has acquired each skill and understanding you identified.

Classroom Observation

"Kid watching" is a natural part of teaching and an important part of evaluation. The purpose of classroom observation in assessment is to gather and record information that can lead to improved instruction. In this booklet, you will find an Observation Checklist (p. AGxv) on which you can record noteworthy observations of students' ability to use science inquiry skills.

Using the Observation Checklist

- *Identify the skills you will observe.*
  Find out which inquiry skills are introduced and reinforced in the chapter.

- *Focus on only a few students at a time.*
  You will find this more effective than trying to observe the entire class at once.

- *Look for a pattern.*
  It is important to observe a student's strengths and weaknesses over a period of time to determine whether a pattern exists.

- *Plan how and when to record observations.*
  Decide whether to

  —record observations immediately on the checklist as you move about the room or

  —make jottings or mental notes of observations and record them later.

- *Don't agonize over the ratings.*
  Students who stand out as particularly strong will clearly merit a rating of *3* ("Outstanding"). Others may clearly earn a rating of *1* ("Needs Improvement"). This doesn't mean, however, that a *2* ("Satisfactory") is automatically the appropriate rating for the rest of the class. For example, you may not have had sufficient opportunity to observe a student demonstrate certain skills. The checklist cells for these skills should remain blank under the student's name until you have observed him or her perform the skills.

- *Review your checklist periodically, and ask yourself questions such as:*

  What are the student's strongest/weakest attributes?

  In what ways has the student shown growth?

  In what areas does the class as a whole show strength/weakness?

  What kinds of activities would encourage growth?

  Do I need to allot more time to classroom observation?

- *Use the data you collect.*
  Refer to your classroom observation checklists when you plan lessons, form groups, assign grades, and confer with students and family members.

Date _____

Rating Scale	
3 Outstanding	**1** Needs Improvement
2 Satisfactory	☐ Not Enough Opportunity to Observe

Names of Students

Inquiry Skills												
Observe												
Compare												
Classify/Order												
Gather, Record, Display, or Interpret Data												
Use Numbers												
Communicate												
Plan and Conduct Simple Investigations												
Measure												
Predict												
Infer												
Draw Conclusions												
Use Time/Space Relationships												
Hypothesize												
Formulate or Use Models												
Identify and Control Variables												
Experiment												

Using Student Self-Assessment

Researchers have evidence that self-evaluation and the reflection it involves can have positive effects on students' learning. To achieve these effects, students must be challenged to reflect on their work and to monitor, analyze, and control their own learning—beginning in the earliest grades.

Frequent opportunities for students to evaluate their performance build the skills and confidence they need for effective self-assessment. A trusting relationship between the student and the teacher is also essential. Students must be assured that honest responses can have only a positive effect on the teacher's view of them and that they will not be used to determine grades.

Student Self-Assessment in *HSP Science*

The assessment program offers three self-assessment measures. In Grades 3–6, an Investigate Self-Assessment is part of each Investigate in the **Lab Manual.** This simple checklist allows students to evaluate their performance, using criteria that are specific to each activity. Two checklists are found in this **Assessment Guide.** One is Self-Assessment—Read and Learn: a form that leads students to reflect on and evaluate what they learned from reading at the lesson or chapter level. The second is the Experiment/Project Summary Sheet—a form to help students describe and evaluate their unit inquiries and projects.

Using Self-Assessment Forms

- *Explain the directions.*
  Discuss the forms and how to complete them.

- *Encourage honest responses.*
  Be sure to tell students that there are no "right" responses to the items.

- *Model the process.*
  One way to foster candid responses is to model the process yourself, including at least one response that is not positive. Discuss reasons for your responses.

- *Be open to variations in students' responses.*
  Negative responses should not be viewed as indicating weaknesses. Rather, they confirm that you did a good job of communicating the importance of honesty in self-assessment.

- *Discuss responses with students.*
  You may wish to clarify students' responses in conferences with them and in family conferences. Invite both students and family members to help you plan activities for school and home that will motivate and support students' growth in science.

Name _____

Date _____

Lesson or Chapter _____

My Thoughts Exactly!

Decide whether you agree or disagree with each statement below. Circle the word that tells what you think. If you are not sure, circle the question mark.

1. The pictures and captions in the book helped me understand what I was reading.   **Agree   ?   Disagree**

2. When I didn't understand, I asked questions.   **Agree   ?   Disagree**

3. I learned a lot from class discussions.   **Agree   ?   Disagree**

4. I used the (Focus Skill) questions and the review questions to test my understanding.   **Agree   ?   Disagree**

5. I understand the new science terms.   **Agree   ?   Disagree**

6. I have a good understanding of the topic.   **Agree   ?   Disagree**

7. I think I am doing well in science.   **Agree   ?   Disagree**

Think about what you learned. Then complete each sentence.

8. Three things I learned about the topic are _____

_____

_____.

9. I learned these new science terms: _____

_____

_____

Experiment/Project Evaluation

Aspects of Science Literacy	Evidence of Growth
I. **Understands science concepts** (*Animals, Plants; Earth's Land, Air, Water; Space; Weather; Matter, Motion, Energy*)	_____ _____ _____ _____
2. **Uses inquiry skills** (*observes, compares, classifies, gathers/ interprets data, communicates, measures, experiments, infers, predicts, draws conclusions*)	_____ _____ _____ _____
3. **Thinks critically** (*analyzes, synthesizes, evaluates, applies ideas effectively, solves problems*)	_____ _____ _____ _____
4. **Displays traits/attitudes of a scientist** (*is curious, questioning, persistent, precise, creative, enthusiastic; uses science materials carefully; is concerned for environment*)	_____ _____ _____ _____

Summary Evaluation/Teacher Comments: _____

_____

_____

_____

_____

© Harcourt

Name _____

Date _____

You can tell about your science project or experiment by completing the following sentences.

My Experiment/Project

1. My experiment/project was about _____
_____
_____.

2. I worked on this experiment/project with _____
_____
_____.

3. I gathered information from these sources: _____
_____
_____.

4. The most important thing I learned from doing this experiment/project is _____
_____
_____.

5. I think I did a (an) _____ job on my experiment/project because
_____
_____.

6. I'd also like to tell you _____
_____
_____
_____
_____.

Portfolio Assessment

A portfolio is a showcase for student work, a place where many types of assignments, projects, reports, and writings can be collected. The work samples in the collection provide "snapshots" of the student's efforts over time, and taken together they reveal the student's growth, attitudes, and understanding better than any other type of assessment. However, portfolios are not ends in themselves. Their value comes from creating them, discussing them, and using them to improve learning.

The purpose of using portfolios in science is threefold:

- *To give the student a voice in the assessment process.*
- *To foster reflection, self-monitoring, and self-evaluation.*
- *To provide a comprehensive picture of a student's progress.*

Portfolio Assessment in *HSP Science*

In *HSP Science*, students may assemble portfolio collections of their work. The collection may include a few required papers, such as chapter tests, performance tasks, and Experiment/Project Evaluation forms.

From time to time, consider including other measures (Science Experiences Record, Experiment/Project Summary Sheet, and Self-Assessment—Read and Learn). The Science Experiences Record, for example, can reveal insights about student interests, ideas, and out-of-school experiences (museum visits, nature walks, outside readings, and so on) that otherwise you might not know about. Materials to help you and your students build portfolios and use them for evaluation are included in the pages that follow.

Using Portfolio Assessment

- **Explain the portfolio and its use.**
  Describe how people in many fields use portfolios to present samples of their work when they are applying for a job. Tell students that they can create their own portfolio to show what they have learned, what skills they have acquired, and how they think they are doing in science.

- **Decide what standard pieces should be included.**
  Encourage students to identify a few standard, or "required," work samples that they will include in their portfolios, and discuss reasons for including them. The Student Task sheets for the performance assessments in this **Assessment Guide**, for example, might be a standard sample in the portfolios because they show students' ability to use inquiry skills and critical thinking skills. Together with your class, decide on the required work samples that everyone's portfolio will include.

- **Discuss student-selected work samples.**
  Point out that the best work to select is not necessarily the longest or the neatest. Rather, it is work the student believes will best demonstrate his or her growth in science understanding and skills.

- **Establish a basic plan.**
  Decide about how many work samples will be included in the portfolio and when they should be selected. Ask students to list on the Guide to My Science Portfolio (p. AGxxiii) each sample they select and to explain why they selected it.

- **Tell students how you will evaluate their portfolios.**
  Use a blank Portfolio Evaluation sheet to explain how you will evaluate the contents of a portfolio.

- **Use the portfolio.**
  Use the portfolio as a handy reference tool in determining students' science grades and in holding conferences with them and family members. You may wish to send the portfolio home for family members to review.

Name _____

Date _____

My Science Experiences

Date	What I Did	What I Thought or Learned

Name _____

Date _____

My Science Portfolio

What Is in My Portfolio	Why I Chose It
1.	
2.	
3.	
4.	
5.	
6.	
7.	

I organized my Science Portfolio this way because _____

_____

_____

_____

_____

_____

© Harcourt

Portfolio Evaluation Checklist

Name _____

Date _____

Portfolio Evaluation

Aspects of Science Literacy	Evidence of Growth
1. **Understands science concepts** *(Animals, Plants; Earth's Land, Air, Water; Space; Weather; Matter, Motion, Energy)*	_____ _____ _____ _____
2. **Uses inquiry skills** *(observes, compares, classifies, gathers/ interprets data, communicates, measures, experiments, infers, predicts, draws conclusions)*	_____ _____ _____ _____
3. **Thinks critically** *(analyzes, synthesizes, evaluates, applies ideas effectively, solves problems)*	_____ _____ _____ _____
4. **Displays traits/attitudes of a scientist** *(is curious, questioning, persistent, precise, creative, enthusiastic; uses science materials carefully; is concerned for environment)*	_____ _____ _____ _____

Summary of Portfolio Assessment

For This Review			Since Last Review		
Excellent	Good	Fair	Improving	About the Same	Not as Good

Grade 4

Getting Ready for Science

Vocabulary

Match each term in Column B with its meaning in Column A.

Column A

_____ **1.** An accepted measurement

_____ **2.** The set of steps scientists follow to find out how things work and affect each other

_____ **3.** An untested conclusion based on observations

_____ **4.** A tool with several lenses that can magnify an object many times

_____ **5.** A statement of what you think will happen in an experiment and why

_____ **6.** A set of steps designed to test a specific hypothesis

Column B

A. hypothesis

B. microscope

C. standard measure

D. inference

E. experiment

F. scientific method

Science Concepts

Write the letter of the best choice.

_____ **7.** Which tool would you use to measure the pull of gravity on an object?
   A. meterstick   **C.** spring scale
   B. pan balance   **D.** thermometer

_____ **8.** What must you do before making an inference?
   F. classify   **H.** observe
   G. communicate   **J.** predict

Name _____

____ 9. What are you doing when you use your knowledge to guess what will happen next?

    A. comparing   **C.** observing

    B. formulating   **D.** predicting

____ 10. A small box is 10 cm long, 5 cm wide, and 5 cm high. What is the volume of the box?

5 cm

5 cm

10 cm

    F. 20 cubic centimeters   **H.** 155 cubic centimeters

    G. 55 cubic centimeters   **J.** 250 cubic centimeters

____ 11. Which tool would you use to measure the volume of a liquid?

    A. beaker

    B. forceps

    C. pan balance

    D. spring scale

____ 12. In which of these is a prediction made?

    F. a dinner menu

    G. a video game

    H. a volcanic eruption

    J. a weather forecast

____ 13. When you describe ways things are alike and ways they are different, which inquiry skill do you use?

    A. compare

    B. conclude

    C. order

    D. predict

Name _____

_____ **14.** Look at the experimental setup below.

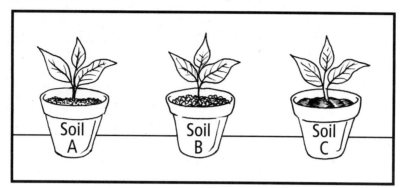

What information would this experiment give?
 F. the effects of light on plant growth
 G. the effects of soil on plant growth
 H. the effects of air on plant growth
 J. the effects of water on plant growth

_____ **15.** What must be controlled in an experiment?
 A. classifications   **C.** graphs and tables
 B. conclusions   **D.** variables

_____ **16.** What are scientists doing when they share the results of their investigations?
 F. communicating   **H.** planning
 G. experimenting   **J.** testing

_____ **17.** What does a pan balance measure?
 A. force   **C.** motion
 B. mass   **D.** volume

_____ **18.** What is usually the first step in the scientific method?
 F. Conduct an experiment.
 G. Draw conclusions.
 H. Communicate results.
 J. Observe and ask questions.

© Harcourt

Name _____

19. A team of students is building a motorized vehicle for a science competition. The students do not yet know how they want to build the vehicle or what materials they need. What can the students do to save time and money before they start to build their vehicle?

_____

_____

_____

20. Tyrone is carrying out an experiment to determine whether rainwater drains more quickly through soil made mostly of sand or soil made mostly of clay. The diagram below shows how he has set up his experiment.

Part A What variable does Tyrone want to test?

_____

_____

Part B Has Tyrone set up his experiment correctly? Explain.

_____

_____

Classifying Living Things

Vocabulary

Match each term in Column B with its meaning in Column A.

Column A	Column B
___ **1.** Probably the oldest living organisms	**A.** bacteria
___ **2.** Having tubes or channels	**B.** invertebrate
___ **3.** An animal with a backbone	**C.** microscopic
___ **4.** Without tubes or channels	**D.** nonvascular
___ **5.** A living thing	**E.** organism
___ **6.** An animal without a backbone	**F.** protists
___ **7.** Algae and protozoans	**G.** vascular
___ **8.** Too small to be seen with the eye alone	**H.** vertebrate

Science Concepts

Write the letter of the best choice.

___ **9.** What are the building blocks of life?
- **A.** cells
- **B.** chloroplasts
- **C.** diatoms
- **D.** organisms

___ **10.** What controls all the functions of a cell?
- **F.** the cell membrane
- **G.** vacuoles
- **H.** the nucleus
- **J.** the nuclear membrane

___ **11.** What are the most numerous organisms on Earth?
- **A.** algae
- **B.** bacteria
- **C.** cells
- **D.** fungi

© Harcourt

Name _____

____ **12.** What kind of plant is shown
in the picture?

   F. hornwort

   G. moss

   H. nonvascular

   J. vascular

____ **13.** How are humans classified?

   A. as invertebrates and amphibians

   B. as invertebrates and fish

   C. as vertebrates and reptiles

   D. as vertebrates and mammals

____ **14.** Why are the plants in the pictures classified as nonvascular?

 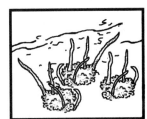

   F. They reproduce by seeds.

   G. They reproduce by spores.

   H. They grow in damp forests and along riverbanks.

   J. They lack tubes for carrying water and food.

____ **15.** How are the cells of bacteria different from all other cells?

   A. They do not have a nucleus.

   B. They do not have a cell membrane.

   C. They are microscopic organisms.

   D. They are multicelled organisms.

____ **16.** Look at the pictures that Amy's teacher drew on the board. She asked the class to find something that all of these creatures have in common. What do you think they have in common?

   F. They are all insects.

   G. They are all arachnids.

   H. They are all arthropods.

   J. They are all crustaceans.

Inquiry Skills

17. Sue wants to make and **use models** to compare vascular and nonvascular plants. To make one model, she wraps green modeling clay around long, thin straws. To this she attaches plant parts of different shapes. To make the other model, she takes a green toothpick and breaks it in half. She glues small pieces of green sponge along the sides of the toothpick. At the bottom of the tooth-pick, she glues small, thin pieces of white sponge. Which model is the vascular plant and which is the nonvascular plant? Explain.

_____

_____

_____

_____

18. Eduardo **observes** an organism with purple tubelike branches rooted to the floor of an aquarium. Eduardo **infers** that the organism is an animal, not a plant. Give a reason he might have made this inference.

_____

_____

_____

Name _____

19. Some bacteria cause disease, but not all bacteria are harmful. List two ways in which bacteria are helpful.

_____

_____

20. Dawn found this drawing of a plant. She has figured out that it's a vascular plant, but she can't determine the kind of vascular plant it is. Use what you know about plant classification to help her.

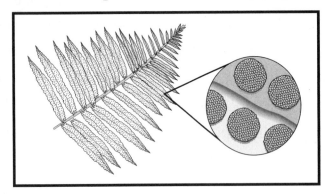

Part A What kind of vascular plant is shown here? Explain how you know.

_____

_____

Part B Dawn is surprised that this plant does not show any signs of budding or of producing a flower. You are not surprised at this. Explain why not.

_____

_____

_____

_____

© Harcourt

Name _____

Date _____

Compare Animals

Materials

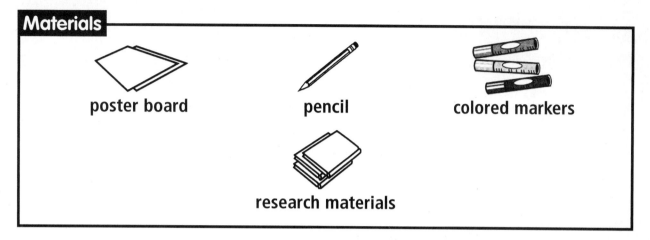

poster board   pencil   colored markers

research materials

Procedure

1 Choose an animal from those listed on the board, or your teacher may assign an animal to you.

2 Work with your group to make a chart, diagram, or labeled picture that helps describe the animal. You may use your textbook and other research materials that you find in your classroom or in the media center. Be sure to include the animal's classification, and tell what it looks like, where it lives, and how it gets food and water. Tell about some characteristics of your animal that are interesting or unique.

3 Choose someone from your group to describe your findings to the class.

4 Join your class in discussing the similarities and differences among the animals.

Compare Animals

Materials   Performance Task sheet, poster board, pencil, colored markers, research materials (located in classroom or media center)

Time   25–30 minutes

Suggested Grouping   6 small groups

Inquiry Skills   observe, compare, describe, communicate

Preparation Hints   Write the names of the following six animals on the board: bird, frog, fish, earthworm, spider, grasshopper. You may want to locate research materials ahead of time and make them available in the classroom.

Introduce the Task   Review with students that classification is based on certain common characteristics. Encourage them to give examples of how plants and animals are classified. Tell students that they are going to illustrate the characteristics of one of the animals listed on the board. Provide an example of another animal, such as an elephant, and lead students to discuss how it is classified, what it looks like, where it lives, how it gets food and water, and interesting or unique facts about it. Let each group choose an animal, or assign one of the animals to each group.

Promote Discussion   When students have finished, ask one member of each group to explain the group's findings. After each report, display the group's poster. After all groups have reported, lead the class in a discussion of similarities and differences among the six animals.

Scoring Rubric

Performance Indicators

_____ Uses a chart or diagram to describe an animal and tell how it is classified.

_____ Researches and accurately records facts about animals.

_____ Communicates the animal's characteristics effectively.

_____ Compares the characteristics of different animals.

Observations and Rubric Score

3	2	1	0

Life Cycles

Vocabulary

Match each term in Column B with its meaning in Column A.

Column A

____ **1.** The basic unit of heredity

____ **2.** A growth process in which an animal gets larger without going through major changes in body form

____ **3.** All the stages an organism goes through

____ **4.** A characteristic that makes one organism different from another

____ **5.** A growth process in which an animal goes through major changes in body form over the course of the life cycle

____ **6.** Processes by which characteristics pass from parents to offspring

Column B

A. direct development

B. gene

C. heredity

D. life cycle

E. metamorphosis

F. trait

Science Concepts

Write the letter of the best choice.

____ **7.** What carries instructions for your growth and development?
  A. your acquired traits   **C.** your family tree
  B. your inherited traits   **D.** your genes

____ **8.** Where do an offspring's genes come from?
  F. The mother contributes all of the genes.
  G. The father contributes all of the genes.
  H. Each parent contributes half of the genes.
  J. Neither parent contributes any genes.

Name _____

____ 9. Which of these traits is determined **only** by heredity?
    A. body size   **C.** intelligence
    B. eye color   **D.** strength

____ 10. After its birth, which animal is most likely to survive and thrive without receiving care from one or both parents?
    F. a bird   **H.** a kitten
    G. a fish   **J.** a seal

____ 11. Which part of a plant feeds the embryo until the plant can make its own food?
    A. the fruit   **C.** the seed
    B. the roots   **D.** the stem

____ 12. How do ferns and mosses reproduce?
    F. from spores   **H.** through pollination
    G. from seeds   **J.** by sending out runners

____ 13. Which of these grow from storage stems called tubers?
    A. ferns   **C.** strawberries
    B. potatoes   **D.** trees, including apple trees

____ 14. How do most animals begin the life cycle?
    F. as a chrysalis   **H.** as a marsupial
    G. as a fertilized egg   **J.** as a nymph

____ 15. Which process does the picture show?

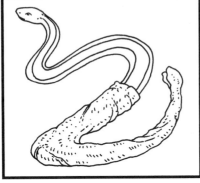

    A. hatching
    B. laying eggs
    C. molting
    D. reproducing

_____ **16.** Which kind of animal goes through direct development?

      F. a frog   **H.** a moth

      G. a grasshopper   **J.** a spider

Inquiry Skills

17. Jorge has planted some bean seeds in potting soil in clay pots and set the pots on a sunny window ledge. Write a **hypothesis** related to which plant part Jorge will **observe** first—the bean pods or the leaves. Explain why you think your hypothesis is correct.

_____

_____

_____

_____

18. Write *1, 2, 3,* and *4* to indicate the correct **order** of development in this animal's life cycle. What kind of development do the pictures show? Explain.

   _____   _____   _____   _____

_____

_____

_____

Name _____

19. Describe the life cycle of the sea horse. What is unique about the sea horse's life cycle?

_____

_____

20. Study the pictures. Use them to compare two plant life cycles.

I 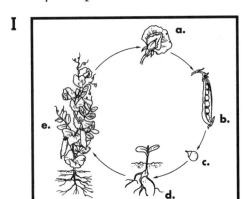   II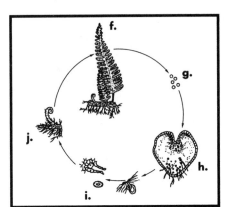

Part A   Which plant produces seeds, and which plant produces spores? Use the letters to identify the seeds and spores in the pictures.

_____

_____

_____

Part B   Which plant life cycle (I or II) includes two separate generations that each produce reproductive cells? Identify the generations by their letters in the picture. What other plants have similar life cycles?

_____

_____

_____

Describe Important Events

Materials

colored pencils or markers

paper

Procedure

1 Draw a comic strip or a series of pictures that shows how your development has been influenced by heredity and by environment.

2 First, think about your life from infancy to the present. Choose five or six events that have taken place in your growth and development. Explain how each event was influenced by heredity and by environment.

3 Don't forget to label your drawings and to add dialogue or explanations as needed. Make sure to use the correct time order to tell what happened.

4 Choose one of the events to share with a partner or your teacher.

© Harcourt

Describe Important Events

Materials   Performance Task sheet, colored pencils or markers, paper

Time   25–30 minutes

Suggested Grouping   individuals

Inquiry Skills   order, draw conclusions, communicate

Preparation Hints   If you plan to use large sheets of paper, you may have to rearrange the room to allow space for students to work.

Introduce the Task   Remind students of some traits and behaviors that are influenced by heredity and of others that are influenced by environment. Explain to students that they will be examining their own life cycles and choosing five or six events in their growth and development that were influenced by heredity and environment. Allow students to be creative, if they wish.

Promote Discussion   Do not ask students to share their comic strips with the class. Instead, hold a general discussion of the ways in which heredity and environment affect development.

Scoring Rubric

Performance Indicators

_____ Illustrates important life events.

_____ Understands how heredity and environment influenced each event.

_____ Draws conclusions about the influence of heredity and environment on growth and development.

_____ Communicates the importance of selected events to his or her development.

Observations and Rubric Score

3	2	1	0

Name _____

Date _____

Adaptations

Vocabulary

Match each term in Column B with its meaning in Column A.

Column A

____ **1.** An inherited behavior that helps an animal meet its needs

____ **2.** Evidence of a plant or an animal that lived a long time ago

____ **3.** A dormant, inactive state in which normal body activities slow

____ **4.** What happens when all members of a species die out

____ **5.** A body part or behavior that helps something live

____ **6.** Animals moving as a group from one region to another and back

____ **7.** Food, water, air, and shelter

____ **8.** Behaviors that were taught to an animal and help it meet its needs

Column B

A. adaptation

B. hibernation

C. basic needs

D. learned behaviors

E. fossil

F. instinct

G. migration

H. extinction

Science Concepts

Write the letter of the best choice.

____ **9.** Which basic need do plants meet by themselves, if they have sunlight?

   A. air

   B. food

   C. shelter

   D. water

© Harcourt

Name _____

_____ **10.** Which is an example of a learned behavior?

    F. breathing   **H.** reading

    G. eating   **J.** sleeping

_____ **11.** Which organism has fossils that show it has changed little over time?

    A. camel   **C.** dinosaur

    B. corn   **D.** turtle

_____ **12.** A woodchuck has just gone into hibernation. Which is most likely to happen?

    F. It sleeps all summer.

    G. Its body temperature goes up.

    H. Its body temperature goes down.

    J. It stops breathing.

_____ **13.** Which organism is **not** extinct?

    A. auk   **C.** saber-toothed cat

    B. ginkgo   **D.** woolly mammoth

_____ **14.** Horses' teeth are adapted for which activity?

    F. eating meat   **H.** eating both meat and plants

    G. chewing grasses   **J.** cracking open seeds

_____ **15.** David watches the birds that come to his backyard feeder. In the winter, there are few birds. In the spring, David makes a chart of which birds arrive first. Why might some bird species arrive at David's backyard feeder sooner than others?

    A. The early birds have a longer distance to travel.

    B. The early birds have a shorter distance to travel.

    C. The late birds didn't know what season it was.

    D. The late birds got lost on the way back.

_____ **16.** A tree falls and rots on the forest floor. The next year, new trees begin to grow in that spot. What is this an example of?

    F. the dead tree growing again

    G. people planting trees

    H. pollution

    J. the cycle of life

Inquiry Skills

17. An ecosystem that you regularly **observe** has changed. You notice the animal populations shrinking. There are fewer plants. **Draw conclusions** about why the animal populations are shrinking.

_____

_____

_____

_____

_____

_____

18. You **observe** a mother cat washing her kittens. When the kittens are older, you **observe** them washing themselves. But you see that kittens without a mother wash themselves less often. What can you **infer** about the kittens' washing behavior?

_____

_____

_____

Name _____

19. The picture shows trees in stages
of a cycle. Describe each stage, and
explain why it is important.

_____

_____

_____

_____

20. Scientists can compare the fossils of prehistoric crocodiles with modern
crocodiles to see how these animals have adapted over time.

Part A What are two things that fossil footprints of crocodiles tell scientists?

_____

Part B Look at the graph. It compares the
sizes of extinct crocodiles and modern crocodiles.
What difference do you see? Why do you think
there is such a difference?

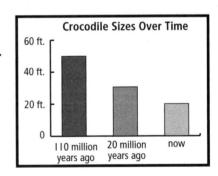

_____

_____

_____

Name _____

Date _____

Animal Adaptations

Materials

colored pencils or markers

Procedure

1 How might the lizard's body parts help it live in the desert?

_____

_____

_____

2 Suppose the lizard's body parts could be changed so that it would be well suited to live in a rain-forest tree. Draw this lizard the way it might look after it had adapted to its new environment. List the changes in the lizard's adaptations.

_____

_____

© Harcourt

Animal Adaptations

Materials   Performance Task sheet, colored pencils or markers

Time   20–30 minutes

Suggested Grouping   individuals or pairs

Inquiry Skills   observe, infer, compare, communicate, make a model

Preparation Hints   Display pictures of a rain forest.

Introduce the Task   Explain that students will imagine a real animal in a completely different environment from its normal one and will draw what the animal would look like if it could adapt to the new environment. Provide examples of how other animals have adapted to different environments. Discuss the characteristics of a rain forest.

Promote Discussion   After students have finished, allow them to view one another's work. Have volunteers explain their drawings and the approach they took. Review the concept of adaptations, emphasizing that real animals would not adapt in a short time, as the imaginary animals did.

Scoring Rubric

Performance Indicators

_____ Identifies various adaptations that an animal shows.

_____ Makes a model or drawing to show how an animal might adapt to changes in environment.

_____ Lists changes in adaptations that would enable an animal to live in a different environment.

Observations and Rubric Score

| 3 | 2 | 1 | 0 |

The Human Body

Vocabulary

Match each term in Column B with its meaning in Column A.

Column A   **Column B**

____ **1.** A hard organ made of three kinds of tissue   **A.** artery

____ **2.** An organ made of bundles of fibers   **B.** bone

____ **3.** A blood vessel that carries blood away from   **C.** capillary
the heart
D. diaphragm

____ **4.** A blood vessel that carries blood back to   **E.** esophagus
the heart
F. muscle

____ **5.** The liquid in which blood cells travel   **G.** plasma

____ **6.** A muscular tube that connects the mouth   **H.** vein
to the stomach

____ **7.** A tiny, thin-walled blood vessel

____ **8.** Muscle that causes breathing

Science Concepts

Write the letter of the best choice.

____ **9.** Where do bones meet?

   A. joints   **C.** tendons

   B. ligaments   **D.** veins

Name _____

_____ **10.** Bones fit together in different ways. Where is there a ball and socket joint in your body?

    F. head   **H.** knee

    G. shoulder   **I.** neck

_____ **11.** What kind of muscles make up the walls of the heart?

    A. capillary   **C.** smooth

    B. cardiac   **D.** skeletal

_____ **12.** In which tube does air travel from your nose or mouth toward the lungs?

    F. artery   **H.** trachea

    G. capillary   **I.** vein

_____ **13.** Muscles work to move bones back and forth. At least how many muscles work together to move one bone?

    A. 1   **C.** 3

    B. 2   **D.** 4

_____ **14.** What is the name of the stringy tissues that connect bones together?

    F. capillaries   **H.** ligaments

    G. joints   **I.** tendons

_____ **15.** Where does digestion in your body begin?

    A. esophagus   **C.** small intestine

    B. mouth   **D.** stomach

_____ **16.** Stella is preparing a report about human skeletons. Which item should **not** be in her report?

    F. The skeleton helps us move.

    G. The skeleton helps us digest our food.

    H. The skeleton protects the organs inside our bodies.

    I. The skeleton supports our bodies and gives them shape.

Name _____

17. Blood moves through your blood vessels and travels all over your body. But sometimes its movement is restricted. **Plan a simple investigation** to find out what happens when your blood is blocked inside a blood vessel. Use a length of tubing, such as a rubber hose, to represent your blood vessels and running water from the tap to represent your blood flow. Write down the steps you would follow.

_____

_____

_____

_____

18. You have done an experiment modeling how quickly different foods would be digested in the stomach. Now it is time to prepare your report and **display the data** you have collected. You have information about the length of time each food took to dissolve and the names of five different kinds of food. What would be the best way to share your data with other members of your class?

_____

_____

_____

_____

Name _____

19. Blood is pumped from the heart to the body and then back to the heart. Use the words *arteries, capillaries, heart,* and *veins* to show the path the blood takes through your body.

_____

_____

_____

20. In order to move blood through the body a pumping action must take place in the heart. The blood then moves through blood vessels to the lungs and the body.

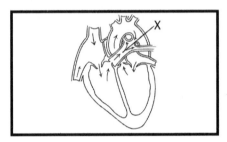

Part A Look at the picture. One vessel is labeled with an X. What kind of vessel is this?

_____

_____

_____

Part B Where is the blood in vessel X going? Explain your answer.

_____

_____

_____

Make a Model of a Muscle

Materials

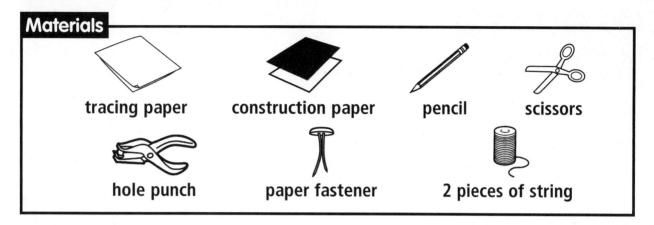

tracing paper | construction paper | pencil | scissors

hole punch | paper fastener | 2 pieces of string

Procedure

❶ Trace the figures at the right onto a sheet of tracing paper.

❷ Cut out your traced figures. Use them as patterns to transfer the figures to a sheet of construction paper.

❸ Punch holes at points A, B, C, D, E, and F. Use a paper fastener to attach the figures at points C and D.

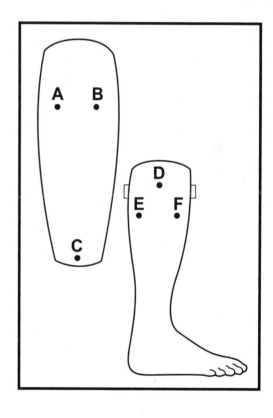

❹ Tie one end of a string through hole E. Thread the other end of the string through hole A. This is string #1. Tie one end of another string through hole F. Thread the other end of this string through hole B. This is string #2.

❺ Pull string #1, and observe and record what happens. Pull string #2, and observe and record what happens.

❻ Write a paragraph that tells how the strings worked as muscles do to move the knee at the joint.

Make a Model of a Muscle

Materials Performance Task sheet, tracing paper, construction paper, pencil, scissors, hole punch, paper fastener, 2 pieces of string

Time 30 minutes

Suggested Grouping groups of two to four students

Inquiry Skills make a model, observe, describe

Preparation Hints Cut strings to appropriate length.

Introduce the Task Ask students to describe a knee joint and tell how muscles work to make the knee move. Tell students they are going to show how muscles work to move a leg forward and back at the knee. Show students an assembled model.

Promote Discussion Ask students to describe the motion they achieved with their models. Continue the discussion by directing students to volunteer information about how many muscles must be used to make both forward and backward movements of the leg at the knee. Ask students to predict what their motion would be like if their muscles didn't function properly.

Scoring Rubric

Performance Indicators

_____ Works cooperatively with other team members.

_____ Constructs a working model of the knee joint.

_____ Observes and records what happens as each string is pulled.

_____ Writes a paragraph that describes how the model simulates movement of the knee joint by the coordinated action of muscles in the upper leg.

Observations and Rubric Score

3	2	1	0

© Harcourt

Write the letter of the best choice.

___ **1.** Which part of a cell is responsible for activities that release energy?
   A. cell membrane
   B. chloroplast
   C. mitochondria
   D. nucleus

___ **2.** What characteristic is used for grouping bacteria?
   F. function   **H.** shape
   G. movement   **J.** size

___ **3.** Which part of a plant makes food and gives off oxygen?
   A. flowers   **C.** root
   B. leaves   **D.** stem

___ **4.** What is the green coloring used in the process of photosynthesis?
   F. chlorophyll   **H.** spores
   G. chloroplast   **J.** starch

___ **5.** What is the largest group of invertebrates?
   A. arthropods
   B. crustaceans
   C. insects
   D. worms

___ **6.** How does water move in a bryophyte?
   F. from cell to cell
   G. from leaves to flowers
   H. from roots to stems
   J. from roots to tubelike structures

___ **7.** What is the basic unit of heredity?
   A. cell
   B. characteristic
   C. gene
   D. trait

Name _____

___ **8.** What is the first stage in a plant's life cycle?

    F. flowering

    G. fruiting

    H. germination

    J. seedling

___ **9.** How is a clone of a plant produced?

    A. asexual reproduction   **C.** sexual reproduction

    B. grafting   **D.** tubers

___ **10.** What is shown in the picture below?

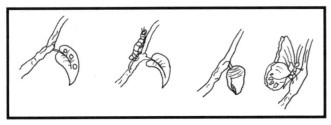

    F. molting

    G. direct development

    H. complete metamorphosis

    J. incomplete metamorphosis

___ **11.** What is shown in the picture below?

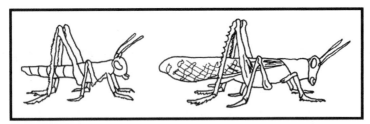

    A. molting

    B. direct development

    C. complete metamorphosis

    D. incomplete metamorphosis

___ **12.** Which mammal does not fully develop inside the mother's body?

    F. cat   **H.** kangaroo

    G. dog   **J.** wolf

Name _____

____ 13. Which of these animals is ready to survive on its own when it is born?
- **A.** birds
- **B.** kangaroos
- **C.** reptiles
- **D.** dolphins

____ 14. What is a body part or a behavior that helps a living thing survive?
- **F.** adaptation
- **G.** basic need
- **H.** instinct
- **J.** nurture

____ 15. Which of these is an example of a living thing following an instinct?
- **A.** a baby learning to talk
- **B.** a child drawing a picture
- **C.** a dog barking at a stranger
- **D.** a horse responding to its trainer

____ 16. Which of these is **not** a reason animals might become extinct?
- **F.** an increase in predators
- **G.** a change in the habitat
- **H.** a decrease in the food supply
- **J.** a seasonal change in climate

____ 17. What do bears do to protect themselves during the winter months?
- **A.** hibernate
- **B.** hunt food
- **C.** migrate
- **D.** travel in herds

____ 18. What do hibernation and migration have in common?
- **F.** They are decreases in body temperature.
- **G.** They are moves from one region to another.
- **H.** They are instincts that help animals meet their needs.
- **J.** They are learned behaviors that help animals survive.

_____ **19.** What is done by both the stem and the roots of a plant?

    A. supporting the leaves

    B. holding the plant in the ground

    C. pollinating flowers

    D. transporting water and nutrients

Write the answer to each question.

20. Compare fungi and plants. How are they alike? How are they different?

_____

_____

_____

_____

_____

21. Suppose an animal moves out of its natural habitat. What do you think might happen? Why?

_____

_____

_____

_____

22. How do scientists infer what animals from long ago looked like?

_____

_____

© Harcourt

Name _____

23. Look at the model of a food web below. Use this model to answer Part A and Part B.

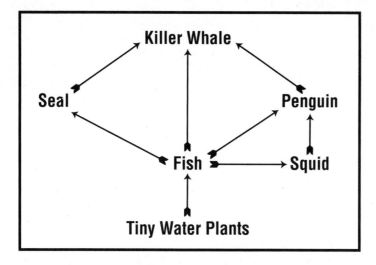

Part A Suppose the fish in this food web become sick and die. What might happen to all the animals that eat the fish?

_____

_____

_____

_____

Part B How might the loss of the fish affect the tiny water plants?

_____

_____

_____

Understanding Ecosystems

Vocabulary

Match each term in Column B with its meaning in Column A.

Column A

____ 1. All the living and nonliving things around us

____ 2. The living and nonliving things in a particular place

____ 3. Having to do with the living factors of an ecosystem

____ 4. A group of the same kind of plant or animal, living in the same ecosystem

____ 5. Work done to repair damaged ecosystems

____ 6. Harmful substances mixed with water, air, or soil

____ 7. All the groups of plants and animals living in the same ecosystem

____ 8. Variety in living things

Column B

A. habitat restoration

B. biotic

C. community

D. diversity

E. ecosystem

F. environment

G. pollution

H. population

Science Concepts

Write the letter of the best choice.

____ 9. Which of these is **not** an example of a nonliving part of an ecosystem?

    A. air   **C.** water

    B. monkey   **D.** soil

____ 10. Which is an example of an abiotic factor?

    F. insects   **H.** water

    G. plants   **J.** trees

© Harcourt

Name _____

Date _____

____ **11.** In which climate would ecosystems have the most diversity?

    A. desert   **C.** taiga

    B. savannah   **D.** tropical rain forest

____ **12.** The diagram shows two populations in a barn community. The cat population has just joined the barn community. Which is most likely to happen?

    F. mouse and cat populations both go up

    G. mouse and cat populations both go down

    H. mouse population goes down as cat population goes up

    J. mouse population goes up as cat population goes down

____ **13.** A landfill closes. The city covers the top with soil and then plants trees. What is this an example of?

    A. a biotic factor   **C.** habitat restoration

    B. erosion   **D.** pollution

____ **14.** Oil drips from cars onto a parking lot. Then rain washes it into a pond, where fish get sick and die. What is this an example of?

    F. adaptation   **H.** population

    G. pollution   **J.** restoration

Name _____

____ **15.** Meesha's lawn is an ecosystem. It includes grass, soil, air, insects, earthworms, and birds. Meesha puts extra water and fertilizer on her lawn. Which parts of the ecosystem will change?

   A. none
   B. all parts, because everything in an ecosystem interacts
   C. just the soil, because she's making it moister and richer
   D. just the grass, because that's why she's adding water and fertilizer

____ **16.** Bittersweet vines grow quickly up trees, where they block light and cause the trees to die. What is this an example of?

   F. trees meeting a basic need
   G. climate changing a population
   H. pollution harming an ecosystem
   J. a biotic factor changing an ecosystem

Inquiry Skills

17. **Compare and contrast** the energy resources used by a car and a bicycle and the effects that a car and a bicycle have on an ecosystem.

_____

_____

_____

_____

18. A highway crew clears the weeds off half of a hillside. After a rainstorm, the weedy part of the hill is the same, but most of the soil is washed away from the bare part. **Draw a conclusion** about the interaction of weeds and soil.

_____

_____

Name _____

19. Describe steps that society can take to reduce air and water pollution.

_____

_____

_____

_____

20. Burrowing owls live in underground holes made by mammals such as prairie dogs. Burrowing owls eat mice, crickets, grasshoppers, and other small animals. Prairie dogs, mice, and grasshoppers all live in grasslands.

Part A What are two basic needs that burrowing owls can meet in a grassland, and how can they meet them?

_____

_____

Part B The graph shows the populations of prairie dogs and burrowing owls in two pastures. Is there a relationship between the number of prairie dogs and the number of burrowing owls? Explain your answer, using information from the graph.

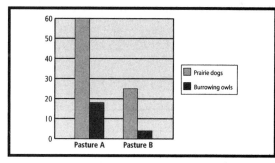

_____

_____

_____

_____

© Harcourt

Name _____

Date _____

Compare Model Ecosystems

Materials

Ecosystem A   Ecosystem B

Procedure

1 Observe the model of Ecosystem A. In the space below, make a labeled drawing to record your observations.

2 Under your drawing of Ecosystem A, list all the *living things* and all the *nonliving things* in the model.

3 Repeat Steps 1 and 2 for the model of Ecosystem B.

<u>Ecosystem A</u>	<u>Ecosystem B</u>

4 On a separate sheet of paper, compare and contrast the two model ecosystems. Use the terms *biotic factor* and *abiotic factor* to explain the major differences between the two models.

Compare Model Ecosystems

Materials Performance Task sheet

Time 25 minutes

Suggested Grouping individuals

Inquiry Skills observe and record, compare

Preparation Hints Prepare and label two model ecosystems. Ecosystem A: Reuse terrarium from Lesson 1 Investigate, or build a new one. Ecosystem B: Pour layers of dry gravel, dry sand, and dry soil into bottle. Place 2–3 dry seeds on top. Cover with plastic wrap and a rubber band.

Introduce the Task Ask students to define *ecosystem* and to give examples of how the parts of an ecosystem interact. Then ask students to define the terms *biotic* and *abiotic*, and to name some biotic and abiotic factors that can affect an ecosystem. Tell students that they will work with two model ecosystems. The two models are different in one important way. The students' task is to observe the ecosystems and identify one factor that makes them different.

Promote Discussion When all students have completed their drawings, lists, and comparisons, ask them to describe the two models. **What abiotic factor was different between the two models? How many other differences were there between the two models? How could you make Ecosystem B more like Ecosystem A?**

Scoring Rubric

Performance Indicators

_____ Produces drawings that are detailed and clearly labeled.

_____ Lists all living and nonliving parts of each ecosystem.

_____ Uses his or her observations as a basis for comparing the two ecosystems.

_____ Identifies water as the abiotic factor responsible for differences between the two ecosystems.

Observations and Rubric Score

3	2	1	0

Energy Transfer in Ecosystems

Vocabulary

Match each term in Column B with its meaning in Column A.

Column A	Column B
____ **1.** Green plants, which make their own food	**A.** habitat
____ **2.** Animals, which cannot make their own food	**B.** consumers
____ **3.** Animals that eat only plants	**C.** decomposers
____ **4.** An environment that meets the needs of an organism	**D.** carnivores
____ **5.** Movement of food energy in a series of organisms	**E.** herbivores
____ **6.** Living things that feed on the wastes and remains of plants and animals	**F.** food chain
____ **7.** Consumers that eat prey	**G.** producers
____ **8.** Animals that eat only meat	**H.** predators

Science Concepts

Write the letter of the best choice.

____ **9.** What is an environment that meets the needs of an organism?

    A. energy pyramid   **C.** food web

    B. food chain   **D.** habitat

____ **10.** From where does a first-level consumer get most of its energy?

    F. predators   **H.** second-level consumers

    G. producers   **J.** top-level consumers

Name _____

____ **11.** Which organism is **not** an omnivore?
   A. hyena   **C.** bear
   B. lion   **D.** human

____ **12.** Where do green plants get most of the energy they need to make their own food?
   F. carbon dioxide
   G. oxygen
   H. sunlight
   J. water

____ **13.** What is the term for the role that each living thing has in its habitat?
   A. food web   **C.** niche
   B. fossil   **D.** prey

____ **14.** Which animal is a carnivore?
   F. cow
   G. lion
   H. mouse
   J. rabbit

____ **15.** What is the term for food chains that overlap?
   A. consumer   **C.** food web
   B. extinction   **D.** producer

____ **16.** Miguel is writing a report about producers, consumers, herbivores, carnivores, and omnivores. Which of the following is a false statement that he should **not** include in his report?
   F. Producers eat consumers.
   G. Herbivores eat only plants, or producers.
   H. Omnivores eat both plants and other animals.
   J. Carnivores eat only other animals.

Name _____

17. How would you **compare** the diet of a carnivore to the diet of a herbivore?

_____

_____

18. Joan saw a mushroom growing on the stump of a dead tree. What could Joan **infer** about the role of the mushroom?

_____

_____

Critical Thinking

19. The diagram shows a simple food chain. Which organism is the producer? Which organism is the first-level consumer? Explain.

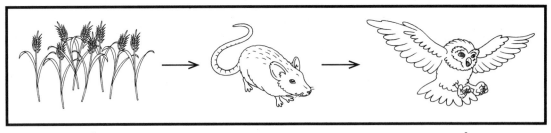

| grain | mouse | owl |

_____

_____

_____

Name _____

20. The diagram shows how energy flows through an ecosystem.

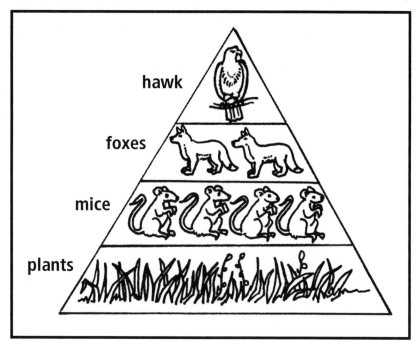

Part A   How does this diagram show that carnivores depend on green plants?

_____

_____

_____

_____

Part B   Why are there fewer hawks and foxes than mice?

_____

_____

_____

_____

_____

_____

© Harcourt

A Food Web

Materials

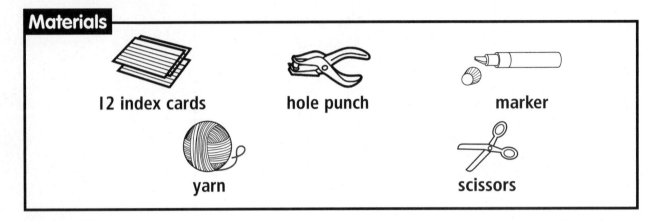

12 index cards   hole punch   marker

yarn   scissors

Procedure

cricket (2)	frog (2)	deer (3)	grass (3)
hawk (4)	mouse (4)	owl (3)	panther (2)
rabbit (4)	shrub (2)	snake (2)	tree (1)

❶ Read the list of organisms. These organisms are part of a food web.

❷ Write the name of each organism on a separate index card.

❸ Look at the list in the box. Each organism has a number next to it.

❹ On each card, punch the number of holes noted next to the name of the organism in the list.

❺ Arrange the cards on your desk so that producers are at the bottom, followed by first-level consumers and second-level consumers, with top-level consumers at the top.

❻ Use yarn to connect the cards to make a food web. Be sure to use all the holes. Compare your food web with those of others in the class. Write a paragraph to describe your food web.

© Harcourt

A Food Web

Materials   Performance Task sheet, 12 index cards, hole punch, marker, yarn, scissors

Time   30 minutes

Suggested Grouping   groups of two to four

Inquiry Skills   make a model, observe

Preparation Hints   Cut a length of yarn for each group. If possible, have an illustration of each organism to show the class.

Introduce the Task   Ask students to describe a food web. Tell them they are going to make a model to show how different organisms interact to form the web. Review the terms *producers*, *first-level consumers*, *second-level consumers*, and *top-level consumers*. Model how to mark cards, punch holes, and tie yarn.

Promote Discussion   Ask students how they chose the order in which to place the cards to form the web. Ask students to hypothesize about the effect of removing any of the producers or first-level consumers from the web.

Scoring Rubric

Performance Indicators

_____ Works cooperatively with other group members.

_____ Follows written and oral directions.

_____ Makes an accurate model of the food web, using all listed organisms.

_____ Writes a paragraph summarizing the relationship of organisms in the food web.

Observations and Rubric Score

3	2	1	0

Write the letter of the best choice.

____ 1. What is used often to name ecosystems?
  A. local rivers
  C. the area's climate
  B. unusual plants
  D. the main population

____ 2. Which ecosystem has the largest number of different living things?
  F. desert
  H. swamp
  G. rain forest
  J. tundra

____ 3. How is the Everglades like all communities?
  A. There are 43 kinds of mosquitoes.
  B. There are many rivers and swamps.
  C. The climate stays warm and wet all year.
  D. The plants and animals depend on each other.

____ 4. Which of these is a biotic factor?
  F. air
  H. sunlight
  G. plants
  J. water

____ 5. Which of these is an abiotic factor?
  A. earthworms
  C. plants
  B. mosquitoes
  D. soil

____ 6. What are you observing when you record the amounts of rainfall and sunlight and the temperature of a region?
  F. climate
  H. surroundings
  G. environment
  J. population

____ 7. Which of these is **not** a basic need of living things?
  A. food
  C. shelter
  B. plants
  D. water

____ 8. What happens when bodies of dead animals decay?
  F. Oxygen is added to the air.
  G. Oxygen is taken from the air.
  H. Nutrients are added to the soil.
  J. Nutrients are taken from the soil.

Name _____

___ **9.** How can people affect ecosystems in a positive way?

    A. by plowing land to plant crops

    B. by clearing land for a new house

    C. by planting a new tree in the yard

    D. by using chemicals to fertilize the lawn

___ **10.** Look at the following list. Which of these are renewable resources?

oil	water
air	sunlight
coal	minerals

    F. oil, air, minerals

    G. minerals, oil, coal

    H. sunlight, air, water

    J. water, sunlight, minerals

___ **11.** Where do 40 percent of the medicines we use today come from?

    A. animals   **C.** minerals

    B. bacteria   **D.** plants

___ **12.** What is a major cause of air pollution?

    F. the fertilizing of crops **H.** the cleaning of drain pipes

    G. the burning of gasoline **J.** the emptying of paint cans

___ **13.**

What do the organisms shown in the picture above have in common?

    A. They are all producers.

    B. They are all carnivores.

    C. They are all consumers.

    D. They are all decomposers.

Name _____

____ **14.** What type of consumer are you if you eat both plants and animals?

    F. carnivore   **H.** omnivore

    G. decomposer   **J.** producer

____ **15.** What does every food chain start with?

    A. consumers

    B. predators

    C. prey

    D. producers

____ **16.** How much energy is passed from one organism to another along a food chain?

    F. 3 percent   **H.** 70 percent

    G. 10 percent   **J.** 90 percent

____ **17.** What might have formed when a plant leaf fell on muddy ground millions of years ago?

    A. fossil   **C.** mineral deposit

    B. organism   **D.** petrified wood

____ **18.** What can scientists learn about an ancient animal from a fossil footprint?

    F. its age

    G. its size

    H. what color it was

    J. what food it ate

____ **19.** Look at the following food chain. Which of these is the producer?

    A. mouse   **C.** hawk

    B. grass   **D.** snake

Name _____

Write the answer to each question.

20. What are three ways in which animals are adapted to survive the winter months? Explain each.

_____

_____

_____

_____

_____

_____

21. Consumers can't make their own food, so they eat other living things. What are the three types of consumers? Explain and give an example of each.

_____

_____

_____

_____

22. What is a niche? How does it help living things and their habitats?

_____

_____

_____

_____

Name _____

23. An ecosystem has both living and nonliving parts. Both parts are needed for an ecosystem to survive. Answer the questions in Part A and Part B to explain why this is true.

Part A   How do plants and animals help each other in an ecosystem?

_____

_____

_____

_____

_____

Part B   What are the nonliving parts of an ecosystem? Why are they important to its survival?

_____

_____

_____

_____

_____

The Rock Cycle

Vocabulary

Match each term in Column B with its meaning in Column A.

Column A	Column B
____ **1.** The changing of rocks over time	**A.** weathering
____ **2.** The bottom layer of soil	**B.** mineral
____ **3.** A layer of soil	**C.** humus
____ **4.** A solid substance that occurs naturally in rocks or in the ground	**D.** erosion
____ **5.** The type of rock that forms when melted rock cools and hardens	**E.** rock cycle
____ **6.** The breaking down of Earth's surface into pieces	**F.** horizon
____ **7.** The remains of decayed plants and animals	**G.** bedrock
____ **8.** The process of moving sediment to other places	**H.** igneous

Science Concepts

Write the letter of the best choice.

____ **9.** Leon says that the soil in his garden feels rough. What physical property of soil is he observing?

A. layers   **C.** shape

B. luster   **D.** texture

____ **10.** Which substance makes up most of Earth's crust?

F. humus   **H.** sediment

G. rock   **J.** soil

© Harcourt

Name _____

___ **11.** What property do all soil horizons share?

    A. bottom layer of humus

    B. partly weathered rock

    C. same types of minerals

    D. upper layer of bedrock

___ **12.** Which property of minerals is being tested in the picture?

    F. luster

    G. hardness

    H. magnetism

    J. streak

___ **13.** Which of these processes does **not** contribute to the weathering and erosion that shapes landforms?

    A. pressure   **C.** waves

    B. plants   **D.** wind

___ **14.** Sometimes two of the plates that make up Earth's surface come together and push against each other. What new landforms may begin to develop as a result?

    F. glaciers

    G. mountains

    H. oceans

    J. sinkholes

___ **15.** Sinkholes occur occasionally in Florida. What causes sinkholes?

    A. Animals dig and move rocks.

    B. Water dissolves underground rock.

    C. Plants grow through cracks in rocks.

    D. Sediment is moved from one place to another.

Name _____

____ **16.** Which layer of soil
contains humus?
  F. Layer F
  G. Layer G
  H. Layer H
  J. Layer I

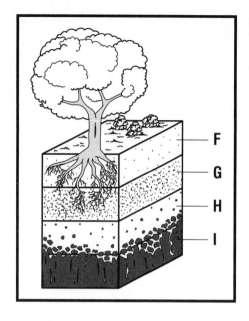

Inquiry Skills

17. You are studying soil samples. You have one with dark soil and one with light-colored rough soil. What can you **infer** about the origins of each?

_____

_____

_____

_____

18. **Compare** rocks and minerals. How are they alike? How are they different?

_____

_____

_____

_____

_____

Name _____

Critical Thinking

19. Rocks are classified into three groups. Name each group of rock, and tell how each type of rock is formed.

_____

_____

_____

_____

20. Miners traveled deep into a mine in search of gold. They found lots of smooth, small stones and some shiny gold rocks.

Part A   To tell whether the shiny rocks were gold or pyrite (fool's gold), the miners decided to do a streak test. Describe a streak test, and explain how it would identify the rocks as gold or pyrite.

_____

_____

_____

_____

Part B   Explain what could have happened over the years to make the small stones in the mine smooth.

_____

_____

_____

_____

© Harcourt

Name _____

Date _____

Weathering and Erosion

Materials

poster board   pencil   colored markers   research materials

Procedure

1 Show how weathering and erosion affect rocks. Use what you have learned in this chapter. Also use research materials that you find in your classroom or in the media center.

2 On the poster board, draw pictures of how weathering and erosion affect rocks. Use a pencil to draw, and then color your picture with markers.

3 Share your poster with the class. Explain how weathering and erosion caused the changes shown on your poster.

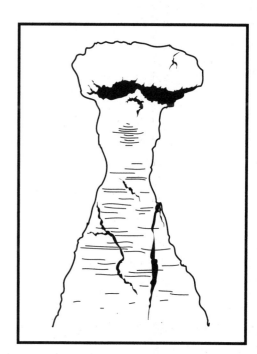

Weathering and Erosion

Materials   Performance Task sheet, poster board, pencil, colored markers, research material

Time   30–45 minutes (You may wish to allow students some time before the project to review the chapter and research weathering and erosion in the media center.)

Suggested Grouping   small groups

Inquiry Skills   display data, communicate

Preparation Hints   You may choose to provide magazines for finding pictures to illustrate weathering and erosion. You and your students may find many other materials to illustrate weathering and erosion.

Introduce the Task   Review the topics of weathering and erosion with the class before breaking into small groups. Allow time for students to brainstorm how they will complete the task.

Promote Discussion   When students have finished, allow time for each group to share its poster. Encourage students to describe how weathering and erosion caused the changes depicted on their posters.

Scoring Rubric

Performance Indicators

_____ Uses research skills to organize information.

_____ Reveals an understanding of the concepts of weathering and erosion.

_____ Assembles illustrations to show how weathering and erosion affect rock.

_____ Communicates findings effectively.

Observations and Rubric Score

3	2	1	0

© Harcourt

Changes to Earth's Surface

Vocabulary

Match each term in Column B with its meaning in Column A.

Column A

___ **1.** A landform that forms where lava flows on Earth's surface

___ **2.** The remains or traces of an organism that lived long ago

___ **3.** The shape of landforms in an area

___ **4.** A landform much higher than the land around it

___ **5.** A large, moving mass of ice

___ **6.** A natural feature of Earth's surface

___ **7.** A shaking of Earth's surface

___ **8.** The dropping of soil and rock by rivers

Column B

A. deposition

B. earthquake

C. fossil

D. glacier

E. landform

F. mountain

G. topography

H. volcano

Science Concepts

Write the letter of the best choice.

___ **9.** Which of these does a plain have?
  A. deep valleys
  B. highlands
  C. mostly flat land
  D. steep cliffs

© Harcourt

Name _____

_____ **10.** How are deltas and dunes alike?

    F. They both form along sandy coasts.

    G. They both form at the ends of rivers.

    H. The movement of fast-moving rivers forms both.

    J. The movement of sand and sediment forms both.

_____ **11.** Why does Earth's inner core remain solid?

    A. It is almost as hot as the sun.

    B. The pressure on it is very great.

    C. The heat around it is very great.

    D. It is made mostly of iron and nickel.

_____ **12.** Which of Earth's layers includes the land that makes up the continents and the land under the oceans?

    F. crust   **H.** inner core

    G. mantle   **J.** outer core

_____ **13.** Where do most earthquakes occur?

    A. along faults

    B. in Earth's core

    C. on valley floors

    D. near coastal plains

_____ **14.** What would you find in the upper parts of Earth's mantle?

    F. fertile soil   **H.** melted rock

    G. iron and nickel   **J.** solid rock

_____ **15.** What causes a tree to become petrified?

    A. The tree is preserved in sap.

    B. Glaciers cause the tree to freeze.

    C. Sediment forms around the tree.

    D. The tree's wood is replaced by rock.

© Harcourt

_____ **16.** Suppose you are a scientist observing this fossil. What might you learn about the animal that made these tracks?

    F. where it might have lived

    G. what foods it might have eaten

    H. what sounds it might have made

    J. how big it might have been

Inquiry Skills

A

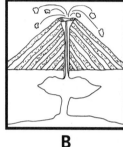

B

17. Observe each diagram carefully. Which one shows a possible shield volcano? How can you tell? Which diagram shows a possible cinder cone volcano? How can you tell?

_____

_____

_____

_____

18. Imagine that Earth's plates have stopped moving. **Predict** what Earth's surface will look like a few million years in the future.

_____

_____

_____

Name _____

19. Palm trees are usually found in warm climates. However, scientists have found fossils of palm trees in Wyoming. What can scientists infer from this fossil record?

_____

_____

20. The picture shows the active volcanoes in the Pacific Ocean Basin. This group of volcanoes is called the Ring of Fire.

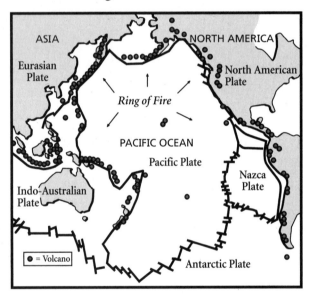

Part A Why is this a good name for this group of volcanoes?

_____

_____

Part B How do you think these volcanoes form?

_____

_____

_____

Name _____

Date _____

Layers and Fossils

Materials

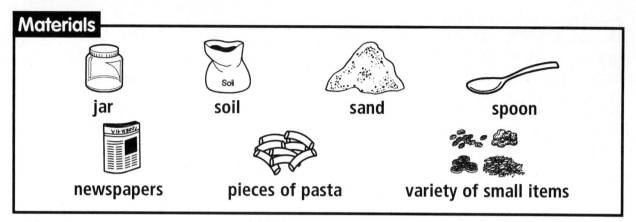

jar   soil   sand   spoon

newspapers   pieces of pasta   variety of small items

Procedure

1 Put a layer of soil or sand in the bottom of the jar.

2 Choose some small items or pieces of pasta to hide in the layer.

3 Add more layers of soil or sand and small items or pieces of pasta. Put different things in each layer.

4 Trade jars with another student or group.

5 Use a spoon to dig the top layer out of your new jar. Spread out the material on a sheet of newspaper. Try to find all the items that are hidden in the layer.

6 Repeat Step 5 with each layer. As you work, record what you find.

7 Draw a diagram to show your findings, and describe the drawing to the class.

Layers and Fossils

Materials Performance Task sheet, plastic jar, soil, sand, spoon, newspapers, pieces of pasta, variety of small items

Time 30–45 minutes

Suggested Grouping individuals, pairs, or small groups

Inquiry Skills make a model, observe, infer

Preparation Hints As an alternative to the materials listed, collect a variety of small items for students to use. You may wish to provide different materials to each group. Sort the materials into small cups or bags to distribute.

Introduce the Task Explain to students that they are going to make a model of layers of sediment. They will hide small items and pasta pieces in the layers. Then they will trade jars with other students or groups, dig out the layers, and make diagrams that show what they find.

Promote Discussion Explain to students that as they record their data, they are also recording the opposite order in which things were put into the jar. Ask students how their work would be different if parts of the layers had gotten mixed up. Ask students what the hidden items might represent and how the diagrams are similar to or different from time lines.

Scoring Rubric

Performance Indicators

_____ Makes a model that represents layers of buried fossils.

_____ Makes a diagram that describes what was found in each layer.

_____ Infers that the hidden things in each layer represent fossils.

_____ Describes the diagram and explains how it is similar to a time line.

Observations and Rubric Scores

3	2	1	0

Write the letter of the best choice.

____ **1.** What do scientists examine to tell minerals apart?
  A. rock cycle
  B. soil horizons
  C. physical properties
  D. chemical weathering

____ **2.** Which of these rocks is formed from other types of rocks by heat and pressure?
  F. igneous   **H.** sedimentary
  G. andesite   **J.** metamorphic

____ **3.** Which happens when you rub a mineral across a surface?
  A. The mineral cuts the surface.
  B. The mineral magnetizes the surface.
  C. The mineral breaks apart.
  D. The mineral leaves a streak.

____ **4.** What is the classification of rocks based on?
  F. their color   **H.** how they form
  G. their shape   **J.** how they heat and cool

____ **5.** What is the sequence of processes that change rock over long periods?
  A. erosion
  B. rock cycle
  C. weathering
  D. mountain building

____ **6.** What causes most weathering?
  F. heat
  G. ice
  H. water
  J. wind

© Harcourt

____ **7.** Which of these is **not** a cause of erosion?

    A. heat

    B. ice

    C. water

    D. wind

____ **8.** What makes up the largest part of soil?

    F. air

    G. humus

    H. sediment

    J. water

____ **9.** What substance forms the hard underlying layer of Earth's surface?

    A. bedrock   **C.** sand

    B. clay   **D.** sediment

____ **10.** What determines soil type and soil color?

    F. the area where the soil forms

    G. different types of organisms

    H. the composition of soil horizons

    J. varying amounts of sand, silt, and clay

____ **11.** What makes soil horizons different from each other?

    A. layers of topsoil

    B. particles of different size

    C. areas of weathered rock

    D. amounts of water and air

____ **12.** Where do dunes form?

    F. in valleys   **H.** along sandy coasts

    G. on mountains   **J.** at the ends of rivers

© Harcourt

Name _____

____ **13.** Which landform is shown in the picture below?

    A. canyon

    B. delta

    C. island

    D. valley

____ **14.** What are you observing when you look at the shape of landforms in an area?

    F. deposition   **H.** fossil records

    G. topography   **J.** Earth's mantle

____ **15.** What happens when two plates along a fault shift quickly?

    A. A volcano erupts.

    B. An earthquake occurs.

    C. A barrier island forms.

    D. A mountain range arises.

____ **16.** Where do most fossils form?

    F. on ice sheets   **H.** in open spaces

    G. in sedimentary rock   **J.** beside petrified wood

____ **17.** What is the main source of clues about Earth's past life and environment?

    A. trace fossils   **C.** fossil footprints

    B. fossil record   **D.** geologic time scale

Name _____

_____ **18.** What new landform may form when two plates push into each other?

  F. delta

  G. dune

  H. island

  J. mountain

_____ **19.** When did dinosaurs live?

  A. Cenozoic Era   **C.** Paleozoic Era

  B. Mesozoic Era   **D.** Precambrian Era

Write the answer to each question.

20. What can scientists learn from studying fossils?

_____

_____

_____

_____

_____

21. What happens during a river's deposition?

_____

_____

_____

22. How can living things cause weathering?

_____

_____

_____

23. Use the following drawing to answer Parts A and B.

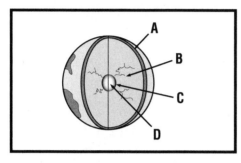

Part A Identify the layers of Earth in the drawing above.

_____

_____

Part B What might you find in each layer?

_____

_____

_____

_____

_____

_____

_____

Name _____

Date _____

The Water Cycle

Vocabulary

Match each term in Column B with its meaning in Column A.

Column A

____ **1.** Instrument that measures air pressure

____ **2.** Process in which water moves from the surface of Earth to the air and then back again

____ **3.** Process by which a gas changes into a liquid

____ **4.** Large body of air

____ **5.** Tropical storm with wind speeds of 119 km/hr (74 mi/hr) or more

____ **6.** Process by which a liquid changes into a gas

____ **7.** Instrument that measures wind speed

____ **8.** Water that falls back to Earth

Column B

A. air mass

B. anemometer

C. barometer

D. hurricane

E. precipitation

F. evaporation

G. water cycle

H. condensation

Science Concepts

Write the letter of the best choice.

____ **9.** Of the following temperatures, which is the lowest at which liquid rain is likely to fall?

A. 0° C   **C.** 16° C

B. 7° C   **D.** 23° C

____ **10.** Sonya listens to daily weather forecasts because she is hoping for a snowy day. Which of these weather changes might bring snow?

F. warm, dry air masses   **H.** cold, dry air masses

G. warm, wet air masses   **J.** cold, wet air masses

Name _____

___ **11.** Where do most storms form?

    A. over land   **C.** in the "eye"

    B. at fronts   **D.** over a peninsula

___ **12.** What might happen when two air masses come together and form a warm front?

    F. steady rain

    G. thunderstorms

    H. a strong sea breeze

    J. cooler temperatures

___ **13.** John is showing his class how liquid water can be changed to other forms. What will happen when he heats the liquid water to a high temperature?

    A. It will evaporate.

    B. It will condense.

    C. It will form clouds.

    D. It will attract dust particles.

___ **14.** Jenny is looking at a drawing of one of the steps in the water cycle. Which of the following describes this step?

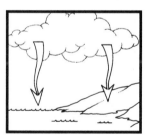

    F. Water vapor rises into the air.

    G. Water vapor is changed to a gas.

    H. Water vapor is warmed by the sun.

    J. Water vapor becomes precipitation.

© Harcourt

Name _____

_____ **15.** Which of these causes flooding during a hurricane?

      A. rain and storm surge   **C.** clouds of a thunderstorm

      B. the "eye" of a storm   **D.** spirals of high winds

_____ **16.** You and your friend are planning a trip to the beach. Your friend does not like walking on hot sand, but he does like swimming in warm water. What time of the day might be the best for you and your friend to visit the beach?

      F. 12:00 P.M.   **H.** 4:00 P.M.

      G. 2:00 P.M.   **J.** 6:00 P.M.

Inquiry Skills

17. The most accurate way to describe weather is to use data from weather instruments. Name three weather instruments you might choose to **measure** the weather, and tell what each measures.

_____

_____

_____

_____

_____

18. Design **models** of two simple weather instruments you could make. Explain how your weather instruments work.

_____

_____

_____

_____

Name _____

19. Think about what happens to water when it falls on land. Explain how rain that falls in your community eventually might end up in an ocean.

_____

_____

_____

20. Strong sea breeze storms happen often in Florida during the summer. These storms frequently form over the center of the peninsula.

Part A   Explain how a sea breeze forms.

_____

_____

_____

_____

Part B   Why do you think these storms form over the center of Florida?

_____

_____

_____

_____

_____

© Harcourt

Name _____

Date _____

Report the Weather!

Materials

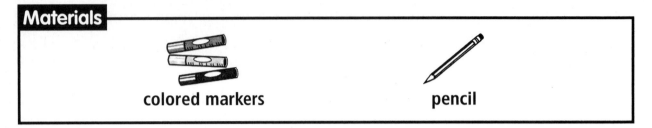

colored markers   pencil

Procedure

Use the information in your textbook, along with what you know
about weather maps, to complete the map below. Use standard
symbols, or invent your own, and different colors to show the following
weather conditions.

- A cold front in the Northwest

- Cloudy conditions in the Southwest

- Rain in the Midwest

- Snow in the Northeast

- Sunny conditions in the Southeast

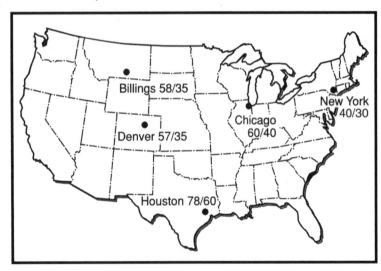

© Harcourt

Report the Weather!

Materials
colored markers
Performance Task sheet, pencil,

Time
20–30 minutes

Suggested Grouping
small groups

Inquiry Skills
communicate, interpret

Preparation Hints
Set up areas where small groups of students can work.
You may want to provide samples of weather maps and symbols for students to review.

Introduce the Task
Ask volunteers to read pages 294–295 in Lesson 4.
Point out the sections that contain information about symbols and colors commonly
used in weather maps. Ask students to discuss other symbols they have seen on weather
maps. Tell students they may be creative; however, the symbols they use must be easily
understood.

Promote Discussion
When students have finished, ask one person from each
group to share the group's map. Have group members explain why they chose each color
and symbol and why they think their map is user-friendly.

Scoring Rubric

Performance Indicators

_____ Uses directions to identify United States regions.

_____ Interprets colors and symbols used to report the weather.

_____ Understands that symbols must be easily understood.

_____ Communicates weather conditions effectively.

Observations and Rubric Score

| 3 | 2 | 1 | 0 |

Planets and Other Objects in Space

Vocabulary

Match each term in Column B with its meaning in Column A.

Column A

_____ 1. The star at the center of our solar system

_____ 2. A small planet-like body that orbits Earth

_____ 3. A large object that orbits a star

_____ 4. A huge burning ball of superheated gas

_____ 5. A large system of stars, gas, and dust

_____ 6. Everything that exists in space

_____ 7. Earth's path as it moves around the sun

_____ 8. An imaginary line that goes through both poles of a planet

Column B

A. axis

B. galaxy

C. moon

D. orbit

E. planet

F. star

G. sun

H. universe

Science Concepts

Write the letter of the best choice.

_____ 9. Kevin is describing the way the moon appears to change shape. What term should he use to describe the different shapes of the moon?

    A. comets   **C.** phases

    B. constellations **D.** satellites

_____ 10. How long does it take Earth to rotate once around its axis?

    F. 1 hour   **H.** 1 day

    G. 12 hours   **J.** 1 year

Name _____

____ **11.** Alana saw a full moon last night. In two weeks, what will she see?

A.

C.

B.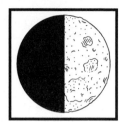

D.

____ **12.** Willa is preparing a report about the outer planets. Which planet should she include in her report?

    F. Mars   **H.** Saturn

    G. Mercury   **J.** Venus

____ **13.** Which two gases make up most of the sun?

    A. oxygen and helium   **C.** hydrogen and oxygen

    B. helium and hydrogen   **D.** oxygen and carbon dioxide

____ **14.** What is one reason that seasons change?

    F. Earth is tilted on its axis.

    G. Earth rotates on its axis.

    H. The sun moves around the Earth.

    J. The temperature of the sun changes.

____ **15.** Mark is wondering why Mars is called the Red Planet. What would you tell him?

    A. All the inner planets are red.

    B. Mars looks fiery red from Earth.

    C. Mars is surrounded by burning gases.

    D. Mars is the closest planet to the sun.

Name _____

_____ **16.** What does a star's color tell us about the star?

    F. how hot it is

    G. how far away it is

    H. whether it has planets orbiting it

    J. whether it is in the Milky Way galaxy

Inquiry Skills

17. Will is **making a model** of the solar system **using numbers.** He found this information about the planets.

Planet	Diameter (kilometers)	Planet	Diameter (kilometers)
Mercury	4,800	Saturn	120,000
Venus	12,000	Uranus	52,000
Earth	12,800	Neptune	49,500
Mars	6,700	Pluto*	2,300
Jupiter	143,000		

*a "dwarf planet"

Which planets will be the largest and smallest parts of his model?

_____

18. It is summer in the Northern Hemisphere. The average temperature in Miami is 28°C. The average temperature in Seattle is 18°C. How do these **measurements** help show the effect of Earth's tilt on its axis?

_____

_____

_____

_____

Name _____

19. Every four years, the year has 366 days instead of the normal 365 days. Why is it necessary to have a year with 366 days every four years?

_____

_____

_____

_____

20. The positions of the constellations seem to change with the season. For example, in the Northern Hemisphere we see Orion during the winter.

Part A Can people in the Southern Hemisphere see Orion when we see it? Explain your answer.

_____

_____

_____

Part B Explain why the stars seem to change position as the seasons change.

_____

_____

_____

© Harcourt

Name _____

Date _____

Day and Night

Materials

ball	I colored pushpin	2 clear pushpins	flashlight

Procedure

1 Push one clear pin into the ball. Push the other clear pin into the ball, opposite the first clear pin. These pins represent Earth's axis.

2 Draw a line halfway between the two pins, all around the ball. This represents the equator. Push the colored pin into the ball, above the equator, about halfway to the clear pin. This represents your location.

3 One student should hold the ball by the two axis pins. A second student should shine the flashlight on the ball. A third student should turn the ball. A fourth student should record the results.

4 Turn the ball so that the flashlight shines directly on the colored pushpin. The pin is in full, direct light. What time does this represent?

5 Rotate the ball one-quarter turn clockwise. Describe the light on the pin. What time does this represent?

6 Repeat Step 5 twice, recording your observations.

Position of Colored Pin	Description of Light on Colored Pin	Time
Original position	Full, direct light	
First quarter turn		
Second quarter turn		
Third quarter turn		

© Harcourt

Day and Night

Materials   Performance Task sheet, ball, 1 colored pushpin, 2 clear pushpins, flashlight

Time   30 minutes

Suggested Grouping   groups of four

Inquiry Skills   use a model, observe, record, interpret data

Preparation Hints   Gather sufficient materials for each group of four students. You may wish to insert the pins into the ball and draw the equator ahead of time. You may also wish to make a full-size data table and distribute copies to students.

Introduce the Task   Ask students to explain why there is day and night. Encourage them to explain the concept of Earth rotating on its axis. Tell students that they are going to make a model that will show how day becomes night and night becomes day. Explain that the colored pin represents their own location and that the clear pins represent the axis on which Earth rotates. Model setting up the experiment.

Promote Discussion   When students have finished, ask them to compare findings and times of day with other groups. Were the findings of the other groups the same? Ask students (as a class) to write a statement to explain how night becomes day and day becomes night. Use a board or an easel board to assemble ideas into a description of the day-night cycle.

Scoring Rubric

Performance Indicators

_____ Constructs an accurate model of Earth, with axis and equator.

_____ Works with other students to show rotation and changing times of day/night.

_____ Observes and records results in the table.

_____ Correctly determines the time of day/night for each quarter rotation.

Observations and Rubric Score

3	2	1	0

© Harcourt

Write the letter of the best choice.

_____ 1. What forms when water vapor cools and condenses on dust particles in the air?
A. clouds
B. precipitation
C. rain shadow
D. water vapor

_____ 2. Which form of precipitation occurs when water vapor turns directly into ice?
F. hail   H. sleet
G. rain   J. snow

_____ 3. What is a fast-spinning spiral of wind that stretches from the clouds of a thunderstorm to the ground?
A. hurricane   C. thunderstorm
B. storm surge   D. tornado

_____ 4. Why do strong sea-breeze storms occur often in Florida?
F. Most of Florida is a peninsula.
G. Most of Florida has a rain shadow.
H. Florida has many land breezes.
J. Florida is a barrier island.

_____ 5. What causes changes in the weather?
A. moisture level of an air mass
B. movement of an air mass
C. separation of an air mass
D. temperature of an air mass

_____ 6. What causes the water cycle to continually occur?
F. evaporation   H. stationary fronts
G. condensation   J. the sun's energy

Name _____

Use the drawing below to answer Questions 7–8.

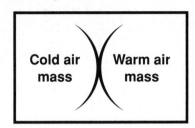

_____ **7.** In the drawing above, a warm air mass is colliding with a cold air mass. What is the border between the two air masses called?

A. eye

B. front

C. rain shadow

D. thunderstorm

_____ **8.** What kind of weather is likely to occur if the warm air mass moves over the cold air mass?

F. hail

G. snow

H. steady rain

J. thunderstorm

_____ **9.** Which picture shows the phases of the moon in the correct order?

_____ **10.** What might be the result if a tropical storm grew stronger?

F. hurricane

G. sea-breeze storm

H. tornado

J. warm front

____ **11.** What separates the inner planets and the outer planets?

    A. gas giants

    B. fiery comets

    C. ring of asteroids

    D. moons with rings

____ **12.** Which of these is **not** an inner planet?

    F. Jupiter   **H.** Mercury

    G. Mars   **J.** Venus

____ **13.** About how often does the pattern of moon phases repeat?

    A. $11\frac{1}{2}$ days   **C.** $29\frac{1}{2}$ days

    B. 24 hours   **D.** 365 days

____ **14.** Which planet was the last to be discovered by scientists?

    F. Earth   **H.** Pluto

    G. Mars   **J.** Uranus

____ **15.** What is the star in the center of our solar system?

    A. moon

    B. comet

    C. universe

    D. sun

____ **16.** What is the smallest planet in the solar system?

    F. Mars

    G. Neptune

    H. Pluto

    J. Venus

____ **17.** Which of these is a huge ball of superheated gas?

    A. asteroid   **C.** moon

    B. comet   **D.** star

© Harcourt

____ **18.** Which of these is in the correct order from smallest to largest?

    F. constellation, galaxy, universe   **H.** universe, galaxy, constellation

    G. galaxy, universe, constellation   **J.** galaxy, constellation, universe

____ **19.** What can you learn about stars from their color?

    A. how old they are   **C.** how hot or cool they are

    B. how far away they are   **D.** how small or large they are

Write the answer to each question.

20. Why does the moon seem to have different shapes, or phases?

_____

_____

_____

_____

21. Where does the information on a weather map come from?

_____

_____

_____

22. Why is Earth considered the most unusual inner planet?

_____

_____

_____

© Harcourt

Name _____

23. Use the following drawing to answer Part A and Part B. Choose from the
following terms to answer Part A: evaporation, condensation, precipitation.

Part A   What is happening at Point A? What is happening at Point B? What is
happening at Point C?

_____

_____

Part B   What happens during the process of evaporation? Give an example.
What happens during the process of condensation? Give an example.

_____

_____

_____

_____

_____

_____

_____

Matter and Its Properties

Vocabulary

Match each term in Column B with its meaning in Column A.

Column A	Column B
____ **1.** Everything that takes up space	**A.** density
____ **2.** The amount of matter something contains	**B.** gas
____ **3.** The amount of space that matter takes up	**C.** mass
____ **4.** Two or more substances that are combined without changing any of them	**D.** matter
____ **5.** A measure of how much material will dissolve in another kind of matter	**E.** mixture
____ **6.** The amount of matter compared to the volume	**F.** solid
____ **7.** Matter that has a definite shape and volume	**G.** solubility
____ **8.** Matter that has no definite shape and takes up no definite amount of space	**H.** volume

Science Concepts

Write the letter of the best choice.

____ **9.** What affects the boiling point of water?

    A. altitude

    B. density

    C. volume

    D. weight

© Harcourt

Name _____

_____ **10.** Which animal would probably have the most mass?

F.    H.

G.    J.

_____ **11.** Which of the following is **not** a state of matter?

 A. density

 B. gas

 C. liquid

 D. solid

_____ **12.** Lori is stirring some salt into water. What is she making?

 F. a gas

 G. solubility

 H. matter

 J. a solution

_____ **13.** Kim is making a surprise gift. She needs material of a definite size and shape. Which state of matter must the material be in?

 A. gas   **C.** mixture

 B. liquid   **D.** solid

_____ **14.** Raphael is grouping different kinds of matter together. Which group contains **only** examples of matter?

 F. garbage, gate, grape, grass

 G. hair, heat, hip bone, horse

 H. leg, lemon, light, lung

 J. sand, soil, sound, sugar

____ **15.** Which has the greatest solubility in water?

    A. oil

    B. paper

    C. sand

    D. sugar

____ **16.** Jorge wants to show that physical properties can be used to tell different foods apart. What physical property would be most useful to tell the difference between mint ice cream and spinach?

    F. color

    G. mass

    H. taste

    J. volume

Inquiry Skills

17. **Compare** the densities below by arranging the substances from least dense to most dense.

Aluminum: 2.7   Gold: 19.3   Iron: 7.9   Lead: 11.3   Silver: 10.5   Water: 1.0

_____

18. Gladys poured sugar into a glass of water and stirred the solution. In time, no more sugar dissolved. Gladys then heated the solution and added more sugar. The extra sugar dissolved. What can Gladys **infer** about the effect of heating on the solubility of sugar in water?

_____

_____

_____

Name _____

19. A diagram of particles of water in the liquid state would show that the particles can move freely past one another. For water in the gas state, a diagram would show that the particles are spread apart and have even greater movement. What would a diagram of particles of water in the solid state show?

_____

_____

_____

20. The graphs at the right show the effect of temperature on the solubilities of two substances.

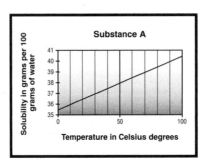

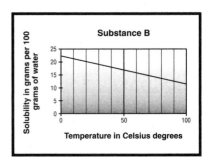

Part A What happens to the solubility of substance A as the temperature increases?

_____

_____

Part B Do both substances behave in the same way as the temperature increases? Explain your answer.

_____

_____

_____

_____

Mix It Up

Materials

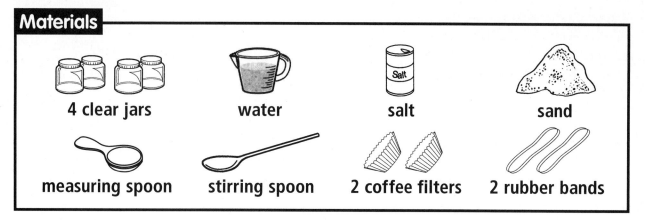

4 clear jars   water   salt   sand

measuring spoon   stirring spoon   2 coffee filters   2 rubber bands

Procedure

1 Half-fill two jars with water.

2 Put $\frac{1}{2}$ teaspoon of salt into the first jar of water. Stir the mixture. Put $\frac{1}{2}$ teaspoon of sand into the second jar of water, and stir.

3 Put a coffee filter in the top of each of the empty jars, and hold the filters in place with the rubber bands.

4 Pour each mixture into a different filter and jar.

5 Complete the following data table.

Jar #	Substance Added	Did substance dissolve?	Did substance go through or stay in filter?
#1			
#2			

6 Compare your results with those of your classmates.

Mix It Up

Materials Performance Task sheet, 4 clear jars, water, salt, sand, measuring spoon, stirring spoon, 2 coffee filters, 2 rubber bands

Time 30 minutes

Suggested Grouping groups of two to four students

Inquiry Skills measure, observe, record data

Preparation Hints Assemble the coffee filters and rubber bands into sets of two. Pour salt and sand into small paper cups for student use. Have students label the jars 1 and 2 before adding water and 1a and 2a before securing the filters on the second set of jars.

Introduce the Task Ask students if all substances dissolve in water. Ask if a dissolved substance can be removed from a solution by filtering. Inform students that they are going to experiment to find out if all substances can dissolve in water and if dissolved substances can be removed from water by filtering. Model the filtering setup.

Promote Discussion Ask students to compare their data. Remind them of experiences they have had with substances that do and do not dissolve. Emphasize that dissolved materials can't be removed from a solution by filtering. Ask students how they could recover the dissolved salt in Jar 1a.

Scoring Rubric

Performance Indicators

_____ Uses materials effectively and works cooperatively with other group members.

_____ Follows written and oral instructions in order to conduct the investigation.

_____ Completes the data table.

_____ Concludes that not all materials are soluble and that soluble materials cannot be separated from a solution by filtration.

Observations and Rubric Score

3	2	1	0

Changes in Matter

Vocabulary

Match each term in Column B with its meaning in Column A.

Column A

____ **1.** A physical change that occurs when matter changes from one state to another

____ **2.** The smallest possible particle of an element

____ **3.** A property that involves how a substance interacts with other substances

____ **4.** A substance made of just one kind of atom

____ **5.** A change that results in the formation of new substances

____ **6.** A substance made of two or more kinds of atoms that are chemically combined

____ **7.** A trait of a substance by itself

____ **8.** A change that does not result in a new substance

Column B

A. atom

B. compound

C. element

D. change of state

E. chemical change

F. physical property

G. physical change

H. chemical property

Science Concepts

Write the letter of the best choice.

____ **9.** Which of these is matter?
  A. energy   **C.** paper
  B. light   **D.** sound

Name _____

____ **10.** Eric has samples of iron, gold, silver, and steel. Which of these is **not** an element?

    F. iron   **H.** silver

    G. gold   **J.** steel

____ **11.** Which of these describes a chemical property of a substance?

    A. colorless   **C.** a liquid at 20°C

    B. odorless   **D.** reacts with oxygen

____ **12.** Which of the following is a chemical reaction?

    F. Hydrogen and oxygen combine to form water.

    G. Liquid water freezes and becomes ice.

    H. A rock is crushed into small pieces.

    J. Sugar dissolves in hot tea.

____ **13.** Saundra heated water until it became a gas. Which term identifies this change?

    A. boiling   **C.** freezing

    B. condensing   **D.** melting

____ **14.** Which is a common physical property of nonmetals?

    F. They are shiny.

    G. They are brittle.

    H. They can be stretched out thin.

    J. They can be drawn out into wires.

____ **15.** Which is **not** a compound?

    A. oxygen

    B. salt

    C. sulfur dioxide

    D. water

© Harcourt

Name _____

_____ **16.** Elena made this chart about water.

Boiling point:	100°C
Melting point:	0°C
Odor:	none
Color:	none

Which is the best title for Elena's chart?

F. How Water Is Formed

G. Chemical Properties of Water

H. Physical Properties of Water

J. Chemical Reactions of Water

Inquiry Skills

17. A chemist heats a white solid. When the temperature reaches 52°C, the white solid melts and turns into a liquid. **Predict** what will happen when the liquid cools below 52°C.

_____

_____

18. Darci has some metal shavings that are attracted to a magnet. Darci mixes the metal shavings with a yellow powder. She then separates the metal shavings from the powder by using the magnet. **Draw a conclusion** about whether a chemical reaction has taken place.

_____

_____

_____

_____

Name _____

19. Jason dissolved a big spoonful of salt in a glass of water. How can Jason show that the salt has gone through a physical change and not a chemical change? Explain.

_____

_____

_____

_____

20. Faith places an iron nail in each of two bottles. She adds water to Bottle 1. Then she closes both bottles. After several days, she notices that rust has formed on the nail in Bottle 1.

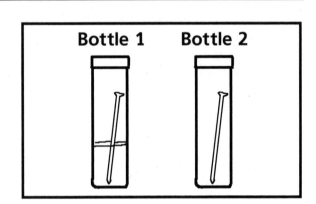

Part A Why did rust form on the nail in Bottle 1?

_____

_____

_____

Part B Why did the iron nail in Bottle 2 not have any rust?

_____

_____

_____

_____

A Chemical Reaction?

Materials

3 calcium carbonate tablets   3 beakers   3 labels   water

white vinegar   cooking oil   3 droppers

Procedure

1 Label one beaker *water*, the second beaker *white vinegar*, and the third beaker *cooking oil*.

2 Place a calcium carbonate tablet in each beaker.

3 To the first beaker, add water drop by drop until the tablet is covered. Record your observations in the data table below.

4 Repeat Step 3 with the second beaker, using white vinegar.

5 Repeat Step 3 with the third beaker, using cooking oil.

6 In the data table, indicate whether a chemical reaction took place in beakers 1, 2, and 3.

Beaker #	Liquid	Observations	Chemical Reaction?
#1			
#2			
#3			

© Harcourt

A Chemical Reaction?

Materials Performance Task sheet, 3 calcium carbonate (antacid) tablets, 3 beakers, 3 labels, water, white vinegar, cooking oil, 3 droppers

Time 30 minutes

Suggested Grouping pairs

Inquiry Skills observe, record, analyze and interpret

Preparation Hints Provide safety goggles for each student. You can prepare the beakers in advance by labeling them and pouring the water, vinegar, and cooking oil into small paper cups for each group. About 10 mL (enough to cover the tablet) of each liquid per group should be adequate.

Introduce the Task Ask students what happens during physical changes and during chemical reactions. Tell students that they are going to observe whether two substances react. Remind them that one sign of a chemical reaction is production of a gas (bubbling). Their task is to determine in which case(s) a chemical reaction takes place.

Promote Discussion When students have finished, ask them to compare their observations with those of other pairs. Were the findings the same? Ask students which liquid caused a chemical reaction. (the vinegar) How could they tell? (A gas was released.) Which liquid caused a physical change? (Water; the tablet broke apart slightly.) Which liquid caused no change? (the oil)

Scoring Rubric

Performance Indicators

_____ Adds liquid to the three tablets and observes the results.

_____ Accurately records observations in the data table.

_____ Determines whether a chemical reaction has taken place in each case.

_____ Explains what the evidence was to indicate that a chemical reaction took place.

Observations and Rubric Score

3	2	1	0

© Harcourt

Name _____

Date _____

Sound

Vocabulary

Use the terms below to complete the sentences.

absorption	frequency	reflection	vibration
amplitude	pitch	transmission	wavelength

1. A quick back-and-forth motion is a _____.

2. _____ is how high or low a sound is.

3. To find out how loud or soft a sound is, you measure its

   _____.

4. The distance from a point on one wave to the same point on another wave is

   the _____.

5. When you measure the number of waves that pass in a second, you find the

   _____.

6. A wave's bouncing off a surface is called _____.

7. _____ stops sound waves from reflecting or
   traveling any farther.

8. _____ means that sound waves keep moving
   through materials to produce sound.

Name _____

Science Concepts

Write the letter of the best choice.

____ **9.** Which unit is used to measure the loudness of common sounds?

    A. decibel   **C.** oscilloscope

    B. electrical signals   **D.** wavelength

____ **10.** Which kind of sound is produced by sound waves with peaks that are very close together?

    F. high   **H.** low

    G. loud   **J.** soft

____ **11.** While hiking, Claud calls his friend's name loudly. What might he hear when the sound waves bounce off the smooth surface of a cliff?

    A. an echo   **C.** a jumble of sounds

    B. silence   **D.** his friend's response

____ **12.** Which part of the ear acts as a funnel for sound waves?

    F. cochlea

    G. eardrum

    H. hammer, anvil, and stirrup

    J. outer ear

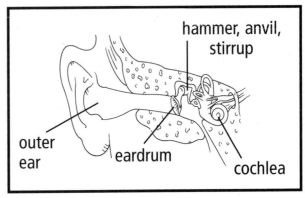

____ **13.** Sound waves cause which part of the ear to vibrate first?

    A. bones   **C.** eardrum

    B. cochlea   **D.** hammer, anvil, and stirrup

____ **14.** In which part of the ear are vibrations changed to nerve signals?

    F. cochlea   **H.** hammer, anvil, and stirrup

    G. eardrum   **J.** outer ear

Name _____

Use the graph below to answer Questions 15 and 16.

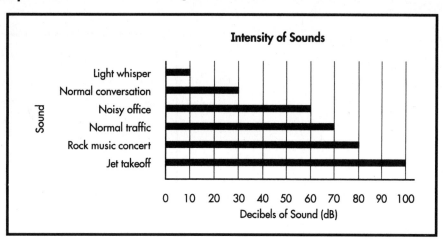

Intensity of Sounds

_____ **15.** Which is softer than normal conversation?

    A. light whisper   **C.** normal traffic

    B. noisy office   **D.** rock music concert

_____ **16.** Which is louder than a rock music concert?

    F. jet takeoff   **H.** normal conversation

    G. noisy office   **J.** normal traffic

Inquiry Skills

17. While riding in a car, you notice that the wheels make sounds against the pavement. The pitch rises as the car speeds up. State a **hypothesis** based on this observation.

_____

_____

_____

18. You want to **experiment** to test how well various materials muffle sounds. Which variables will you keep the same? Which variable will you change?

_____

_____

Name _____

Critical Thinking

19. Which instrument plays at a higher pitch? Why?

bass   violin

_____

_____

_____

20. Peyton is standing at her front door. Her friend Omar is five houses down the street. Peyton yells, "Omar!"

Part A How is the sound of Peyton's voice transmitted to Omar?

_____

_____

Part B Omar doesn't hear Peyton when she calls. When she calls again, what are two things she can do to make sure Omar hears her?

_____

_____

_____

© Harcourt

Name _____

Date _____

Compare Pitches

Materials

4 bottles

water

ruler

Procedure

1 Put a different amount of water in each bottle, from the least water in Bottle 1 to the most water in Bottle 4.

2 Measure the height of the water in each bottle, and record the heights in the data table below.

3 Predict how the different levels of water will affect pitch.

4 Blow across the mouth of Bottle 1. Does the sound have a high pitch or a low one? Record in the table your observation of the pitch.

5 Blow across the mouth of Bottle 2. Does the sound have a higher pitch or a lower pitch than the sound of Bottle 1? Blow again across the tops of Bottles 1 and 2 to make sure. Record your observations.

6 Repeat Step 5 with Bottle 3 and Bottle 4. Record your observations. Compare your prediction with the results you obtained.

	Bottle 1	Bottle 2	Bottle 3	Bottle 4
Height of water column				
Pitch of sound				

© Harcourt

Compare Pitches

Materials   Performance Task sheet, 4 bottles, water, ruler

Time   30 minutes

Suggested Grouping   pairs or groups of three

Inquiry Skills   observe, compare, infer

Preparation Hints   Collect sets of four same-size bottles for students to use.

Introduce the Task   Ask students to recall what they know about how trombones and other wind instruments change pitch. Make sure they understand that pitch is affected by the length of the air column and the change in frequency of the sound waves. Ask students to predict how different levels of water in a bottle will affect pitch.

Promote Discussion   When students finish, ask them to share their results. Were their results similar? Did they find that the higher the water level, the higher the pitch? Ask students to explain the relationship between water level, the corresponding height of the column of air above the water, and pitch. (The higher the water level, the shorter the column of air. The shorter the column of air, the higher the pitch. This is because the shorter column of air in a fuller bottle vibrates at a higher frequency than the longer column of air in a less-full bottle.) Ask students to compare their predictions with their results.

Scoring Rubric

Performance Indicators

_____ Sets up and properly conducts experiment.

_____ Records data accurately for each bottle.

_____ Compares predictions with experimental results.

_____ Determines that the shorter the column of air, the higher the pitch.

Observations and Rubric Score

3	2	1	0

Light and Heat

Vocabulary

Match each term in Column B with its meaning in Column A.

Column A

____ **1.** A form of energy that can travel through space

____ **2.** Light bouncing off an object

____ **3.** Light bending when it changes speed

____ **4.** Heat that can't be used to do work

____ **5.** The way heat travels through materials that are touching

____ **6.** The movement of heat in liquids and gases

____ **7.** The movement of heat without matter

____ **8.** The change of energy from one form to another

Column B

A. refraction

B. radiation

C. convection

D. light

E. waste heat

F. reflection

G. energy transfer

H. conduction

Science Concepts

Write the letter of the best choice.

____ **9.** Sasha pulls down a window shade to block the sunlight completely. Which word describes the window shade?

A. opaque

B. radiant

C. translucent

D. transparent

____ **10.** Vahid places a pan on a hot electric stove burner. How does the burner heat the pan?

    F. conduction

    G. convection

    H. radiation

    J. reflection

____ **11.** All cups are full. Which cup has the most energy?

    A. cup 1

    B. cup 2

    C. cup 3

    D. Cup 1 and cup 2 have the same total energy.

____ **12.** What happens to light when it hits a mirror?

    F. It reflects.   **H.** It is absorbed.

    G. It refracts.   **J.** It passes through.

____ **13.** Which example of matter would carry heat by convection?

    A. bread

    B. lemonade

    C. sand

    D. seashells

____ **14.** When a thermometer is warmed, the liquid inside it rises. While this is happening, what is true about the particles of the liquid?

    F. They move less.

    G. They stop vibrating.

    H. They move more slowly.

    J. They have more energy.

____ **15.** Emily is watching bread bake in an oven. The oven door is closed, but it is warm next to the oven. What is warming Emily?

    A. reflection

    B. refraction

    C. solar power

    D. waste heat

____ **16.** What does temperature measure?

    F. heat in matter

    G. heat absorbed by matter

    H. total energy transferred by matter

    J. average energy of particles in matter

Inquiry Skills

17. An artist puts a piece of metal into a vat of water. The temperature of the water rises. What can you **infer** about the original temperature of the metal and the water?

_____

_____

_____

18. A turkey should be cooked until it is 86°C. An oven cooks a turkey by conduction. Where should you put a thermometer to **measure** whether the whole turkey is done cooking?

_____

_____

_____

© Harcourt

Name _____

19. Marisol and Anita are visiting the bookmobile. Marisol is standing in the sun. Anita is standing in the shade.

Which girl can see the sun? Explain.

_____

_____

_____

20. The picture shows two solar cookers. One is clean and shiny. The other is dirty and dull. Everything else about the cookers is the same.

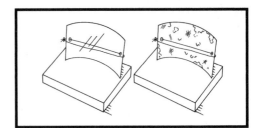

Part A Which cooker will reach a higher temperature?

_____

Part B Explain why the cooker you chose will reach a higher temperature.

_____

_____

_____

© Harcourt

Name _____

Date _____

Observing Convection

Materials

tape

water

container

dyed ice cube

2 thermometers

clock

Procedure

1 Set up the materials as shown. Fill the container with water. Tape one thermometer so that its bulb is near the top of the water.

2 Wait 1 minute. Then record the temperatures in the table row for 0 min.

3 Place the dyed ice cube in the water. Keep it away from the thermometers. DO NOT STIR THE WATER.

4 Start timing. Record the temperatures every minute for 5 minutes. Observe the dye while you wait.

5 Find the difference between the first and last temperatures for each thermometer. Record the differences in the table.

6 Describe the convection that took place in the container. Use your data and observations.

7 Predict what will happen to the temperature if you let the container sit for 10 more minutes.

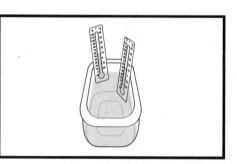

Time (min)	Temperature (°C)	
	Top	Bottom
0		
1		
2		
3		
4		
5		
Difference		

© Harcourt

Observing Convection

Materials
Performance Task sheet, 2 thermometers, clear tape, clock, 3-cup rectangular food-storage container, water, plastic jugs, ice-cube trays, dark food coloring

Time
30 minutes

Suggested Grouping
pairs

Inquiry Skills
observe, measure, record, predict

Preparation Hints
Use containers of the size and shape listed. You will need access to a freezer. *Day before:* Fill ice-cube trays with water, and add 1 to 2 drops of dark food coloring to each well. Let the water freeze overnight. Fill the jugs with water, and let them sit overnight to reach room temperature. Tell students to tape the thermometers so that the bulb of one is at the bottom of the container and the bulb of the other is near the top, but covered with water.

Introduce the Task
Review how convection starts in a pot on a stove: water at the bottom is heated, and then cool water moves in, pushing the heated water up. Tell students that the cool water is then heated and is also pushed up. In this investigation, they are going to observe convection by using two kinds of tools: a dye that makes cold water visible and two thermometers.

Promote Discussion
Ask students to describe the path the cold water took as the ice cube melted. **What must have happened to the warmer water as the colder water moved in? How does the temperature data show the movement of the water?**

Scoring Rubric

Performance Indicators

_____ Follows the diagram to correctly set up the equipment.

_____ Makes all temperature readings and records them in the table.

_____ Describes the convection in detail.

_____ Bases prediction on own data and observations.

Observations and Rubric Score

3	2	1	0

Write the letter of the best choice.

____ **1.** Which of these always takes up the same amount of space and keeps its shape?

    A. gas

    B. liquid

    C. matter

    D. solid

____ **2.** Which of these is **not** a physical property of matter?

    F. mass   **H.** ability to burn

    G. volume   **J.** ability to conduct heat

____ **3.** What is the result of the flowing of thermal energy from warmer to cooler objects?

    A. change of state

    B. electrical property

    C. heat

    D. temperature

____ **4.** An object has a mass of 16 grams and a volume of 4 cubic centimeters. What is its density?

    F. 4 g/cm^3 **H.** 20 g/cm^3

    G. 12 g/cm^3 **J.** 64 g/cm^3

____ **5.** Which of these substances is a liquid at $-10°C$?

    A. iron

    B. mercury

    C. oxygen

    D. water

____ **6.** What is the smallest possible particle of a substance?

    F. atom   **H.** grain

    G. element   **J.** matter

Name _____

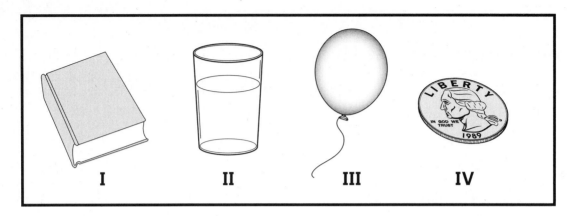

I   II   III   IV

___ **7.** Which of the objects pictured above contains material with a definite volume, but no definite shape?

    A. I

    B. II

    C. III

    D. IV

___ **8.** Which change of state occurs when a gas cools?

    F. boiling

    G. condensing

    H. freezing

    J. melting

___ **9.** Which of these involves a change of state that results in a new substance?

    A. burning wood

    B. carving stone

    C. dissolving sugar

    D. melting ice

___ **10.** Which of the following is a physical change?

    F. baking bread

    G. burning wood

    H. cutting an apple

    J. rusting iron

Name _____

_____ **11.** Which of these involves a chemical change?
    A. baking bread
    B. boiling water
    C. cutting wood
    D. freezing water

_____ **12.** Which of these is a clue that a chemical change is probably taking place?
    F. change in size   **H.** change in color
    G. change in state   **J.** change in shape

_____ **13.** Which of these would produce a sound with a low pitch and loud intensity?
    A. baby crying   **C.** large dog barking
    B. child whispering   **D.** small dog barking

_____ **14.** Which of these is **not** used to describe sound waves?
    F. amplitude
    G. frequency
    H. transverse
    J. wavelength

_____ **15.** What happens to sound in a carpeted room?
    A. absorption   **C.** transmission
    B. reflection   **D.** vibration

_____ **16.** Which of these materials is opaque?
    F. brick wall   **H.** clear plastic
    G. clear glass   **J.** wax paper

_____ **17.** How is heat carried in an empty space, where there is no matter?
    A. conduction
    B. convection
    C. radiation
    D. thermal energy

Name _____

___ **18.** Which use of heat makes changes in matter?

      F. bathing bodies   **H.** melting metals

      G. heating homes   **J.** washing clothes

___ **19.** What is Earth's main source of heat and light?

      A. gas   **C.** sun

      B. oil   **D.** wood

Write the answer to each question.

20. When you shout down a long, narrow hall, why do you sometimes hear an echo?

_____

_____

_____

21. Why is your shadow behind you when you face the sunlight?

_____

_____

_____

_____

_____

22. How can you prove that air has mass?

_____

_____

_____

_____

Name _____

23. Use the data in the following table to answer Part A and Part B.

Process	Clue
1. chopping wood	logs or splinters
2. burning wood	ash; smell of smoke
3. frying eggs	becomes firm; color changes
4. shredding paper	thin strips

Part A Interpret the data in the table to infer whether a physical or a chemical change occurs in each process.

_____

_____

_____

Part B What happens to a substance during a physical change? What happens to a substance during a chemical change?

_____

_____

_____

_____

Name _____

Date _____

Making and Using Electricity

Vocabulary

Match each term in Column B with its meaning in Column A.

Column A

____ **1.** A material that lets electricity travel through it easily

____ **2.** An electrical charge that builds up in an object

____ **3.** An object that attracts iron

____ **4.** A temporary magnet

____ **5.** A machine that produces electric current

____ **6.** The energy of motion

____ **7.** A path that has more than one way an electric current can flow

____ **8.** Energy an object has because of its position or condition

Column B

A. conductor

B. electromagnet

C. generator

D. parallel circuit

E. magnet

F. kinetic energy

G. potential energy

H. static electricity

Science Concepts

Write the letter of the best choice.

____ **9.** What is stored in the bonds that hold compounds together?

   A. chemical energy   **C.** magnets

   B. insulators   **D.** static electricity

____ **10.** What kind of energy is also called energy of position?

   F. generator   **H.** motor

   G. kinetic   **J.** potential

© Harcourt

Name _____

_____ **11.** What is the name of a path that has only one way for the current to flow?

    A. current electricity

    B. magnetic field

    C. power field

    D. series circuit

— battery
⊗ light bulb

_____ **12.** Which is a good conductor of electricity?

    F. copper

    G. glass

    H. plastic

    J. rubber

_____ **13.** Jack and his family visited a large dam, where they were told that the kinetic energy of falling water was changed to electrical energy. What kind of power did this dam produce?

    A. chemical power   **C.** geothermal power

    B. hydroelectric power   **D.** solar power

_____ **14.** What is a stream of electrons moving through a copper wire called?

    F. current electricity

    G. generator

    H. magnetic field

    J. motor

_____ **15.** Todd wants to build a small electric generator. What two items must he have to make his generator?

    A. coal and oil

    B. coil of wire and magnet

    C. steam and turbine

    D. wire and switch

____ **16.** A magnet will hold papers to a refrigerator, but papers are not attracted to a magnet. What can be concluded about the refrigerator, the magnet, and the papers?

  F. The refrigerator, the magnet, and the papers are all magnetic.

  G. The refrigerator and the magnet become magnetized by the papers.

  H. Magnetic forces pass from the papers to both the refrigerator and the magnet.

  J. Magnetic forces pass from the magnet, through the papers, to the refrigerator.

Inquiry Skills

17. Offices, homes, and factories each use about the same amount of electricity. If you made a pie graph to **compare** the amounts used, what fraction of the graph would be labeled for each kind of user?

_____

_____

18. Suppose you are testing the strength of an electromagnet. You are changing the number of loops of wire. You are measuring how many paper clips the electromagnet can pick up. Describe a table that you would use to **record the data.**

_____

_____

_____

_____

© Harcourt

Name _____

Critical Thinking

19. Batteries supply a stream of electrons to power toys and electronics. When some batteries wear out, they can be recharged. Explain how this might be possible.

_____

_____

_____

20. Electrical devices can be wired together in different ways.

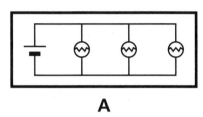

A

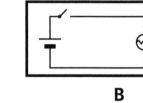

B

Key
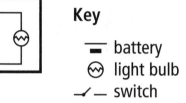
— battery
⊗ light bulb
⌐⁄— switch

Part A   Figure A shows a circuit. When one light bulb is removed, the others stay lit. Is this a parallel circuit or a series circuit? Explain.

_____

_____

_____

_____

Part B   Figure B shows a switch in an electrical circuit. Is the switch part of the circuit in a series connection or in a parallel connection? Explain.

_____

_____

_____

Name _____

Date _____

Magnetic Poles

Materials

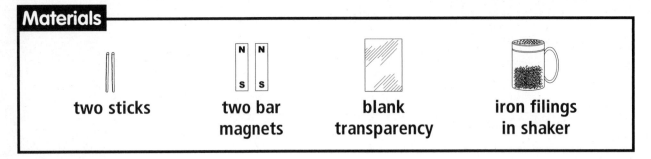

two sticks

two bar magnets

blank transparency

iron filings in shaker

Procedure

1 Place the two sticks on a flat table, parallel to each other and about 15 cm apart.

2 Place a bar magnet halfway between the sticks, as shown in Figure A.

3 Place a blank transparency over the magnet and sticks. Lightly sprinkle iron filings on top of the transparency, all over the magnet. Make a labeled sketch of the magnet and the pattern formed by the iron filings.

4 Use the transparency to pour the filings back into the shaker.

5 Repeat Steps 1, 2, and 3, but place the two magnets as shown in Figure B. Then repeat these steps again, placing the two magnets as shown in Figure C.

6 Write a paragraph to describe and explain your observations.

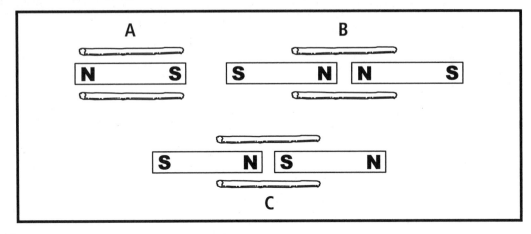

© Harcourt

Magnetic Poles

Materials   Performance Task sheet, two
sticks, two bar magnets, blank transparency, iron filings in shaker

Time   30 minutes

Suggested Grouping   groups of two to four students

Inquiry Skills   observe, draw conclusions

Preparation Hints   Pour iron filings into grated-cheese shakers or salt
shakers with large holes. Make sure sticks are about the same thickness as magnets.

Introduce the Task   Ask students to describe a magnet. Guide them to use
the term *poles* to describe the ends of a bar magnet. Tell them they are going to do an
investigation to see the effect that poles have on iron filings and on each other. Model
the setups they are to use.

Promote Discussion   Ask students to describe the results of their investigation.
Direct the discussion toward the fact that there was a "field" around each pole. Continue
the discussion so that students comprehend that unlike poles attract each other and like
poles repel each other. Ask students to display their drawings.

Scoring Rubric

Performance Indicators

_____ Works cooperatively with other team members.

_____ Follows written and oral directions.

_____ Makes three labeled drawings to show the positions of the magnets and
iron filings.

_____ Writes a paragraph and concludes that like poles of a magnet repel and unlike
poles attract.

Observations and Rubric Score

3	2	1	0

Name _____

Date _____

Forces and Motion

Vocabulary

Match each term in Column B with its meaning in Column A.

Column A

Column B

____ **1.** A force that acts between all masses and causes them to attract one another

A. acceleration

____ **2.** The change of position during a unit of time

B. force

____ **3.** The speed and direction of an object

C. gravity

____ **4.** A push or a pull

D. inertia

____ **5.** The force of attraction between Earth and other objects

E. gravitation

____ **6.** A force that resists motion, relative to each other, of objects that are touching

F. friction

G. speed

____ **7.** A change in speed or direction of an object's motion

H. velocity

____ **8.** The property of matter that keeps a moving object moving in a straight line

Science Concepts

Write the letter of the best choice.

____ **9.** What is the measurement of the force of gravity on an object?
   A. acceleration   **C.** speed
   B. mass   **D.** weight

____ **10.** Which force resists motion between objects that are in contact?
   F. friction   **H.** speed
   G. mass   **J.** velocity

Name _____

_____ **11.** Which one of the following causes acceleration?

    A. force

    B. inertia

    C. speed

    D. weight

_____ **12.** What is the least number of photographs needed to tell if a horse is moving?

    F. 1

    G. 2

    H. 7

    J. 100

_____ **13.** Henri wants to explain what is meant by mass. How should he describe the mass of his body?

    A. the weight of his body in newtons

    B. the weight of his body in pounds

    C. the volume occupied by his body

    D. the amount of matter in his body

_____ **14.** Which type of force causes a boy jumping off a chair to move toward Earth?

    F. buoyant

    G. electrical

    H. gravitational

    J. magnetic

_____ **15.** What two things must Stephanie measure to find the speed of a moving bicycle?

    A. mass and inertia

    B. distance and time

    C. gravity and friction

    D. position and motion

_____ **16.** After studying acceleration, Amos explains why the gas pedal in a car is called an accelerator. What should Amos say in his explanation?

    F. An accelerator increases friction.

    G. An accelerator causes a change in the car's velocity.

    H. An accelerator balances the effect of gravitational force.

    J. An accelerator is used to keep the velocity the same.

Inquiry Skills

17. List the tools you need to **measure** speed. Tell how you would use them.

_____

_____

_____

_____

18. Suppose you are a scientist who has just finished an experiment to test the effects of friction on motion. What information about your experiment would you **communicate** to another scientist so that he or she could check your results?

_____

_____

_____

© Harcourt

Critical Thinking

19. Margaret watched a magician pull a tablecloth out from under a set of dishes without moving the dishes. What property of matter was Margaret observing? Explain.

_____

_____

_____

20. Diagram A shows a 2-kilogram pillow and a 2-kilogram brick. Diagram B shows a 1-kilogram pillow and a 1-kilogram brick.

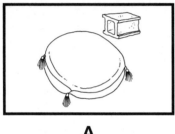   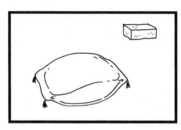

A   **B**

Part A   Does the 2-kilogram pillow have twice as much mass as the 1-kilogram pillow? Explain.

_____

_____

Part B   Where would the 1-kilogram pillow weigh half as much as the 2-kilogram brick?

_____

_____

_____

Don't Move!

Materials

sheet of paper   ruler   pencil   full can of soda

Procedure

1 Make a dot on a sheet of paper, 2 inches from one end and centered.

2 Place the sheet of paper on a clean, dry desktop so that about one-third of the paper is over the edge. Make sure the end with the dot is on the desktop. Put a full, dry, unopened can of soda on the dot.

3 Hold the end of the paper that is hanging over the edge of the desktop.

4 Give the paper a quick jerk away from the can and the desk.

5 Repeat Step 4 several times.

6 Write a paragraph that describes what you did and what you observed. Give a reason for what happened.

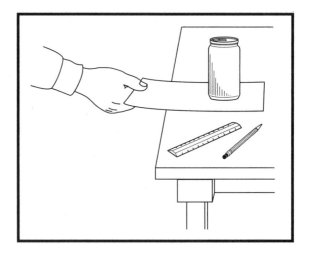

© Harcourt

Don't Move!

Materials Performance Task sheet, sheet of paper, ruler, pencil, full can of soda

Time 25 minutes

Suggested Grouping pairs

Inquiry Skills observe, draw conclusions

Preparation Hints Have warm cans of soda that will not allow condensation to form on the outside.

Introduce the Task Tell students that they will see how inertia works. Ask them to define *inertia*. Write the definition on the board. Tell students that it may take several attempts before they are able to jerk the paper smoothly to demonstrate inertia. Model the setup they are to use.

Promote Discussion Ask students why the soda can stayed in place. Direct the discussion toward the fact that inertia is a physical property that keeps items at rest unless acted upon by an outside force. Inertia also keeps moving things moving. Extend the concept by demonstrating the same effect with other objects on a piece of paper or cloth.

Scoring Rubric

Performance Indicators

_____ Works cooperatively with other team members.

_____ Follows written and oral directions.

_____ Repeats activity several times until soda can stays at rest.

_____ Writes paragraph and concludes that inertia is responsible for the can's staying in place when the paper is jerked.

Observations and Rubric Score

3	2	1	0

Name _____

Date _____

Simple Machines

Vocabulary

Match each term in Column B with its meaning in Column A.

Column A	Column B
____ **1.** A machine with few or no moving parts, to which only one force is applied	**A.** pulley
____ **2.** Two inclined planes placed back to back	**B.** work
____ **3.** The fixed point on a lever	**C.** inclined plane
____ **4.** The use of force to move an object over a distance	**D.** simple machine
____ **5.** A wheel with a line around it	**E.** lever
____ **6.** A bar that pivots on a fixed point	**F.** wedge
____ **7.** A post with threads wrapped around it	**G.** screw
____ **8.** A slanted surface	**H.** fulcrum

Science Concepts

____ **9.** Scientists have a special meaning for *work*. Which one of these is an example of scientific work?

    A. pushing on a door that won't open

    B. lifting a box off the floor

    C. standing still with a backpack strapped to your back

    D. reading a textbook

Name _____

_____ **10.** What must a wheel and an axle do to be a simple machine?

       F. The wheel and the axle must turn together.

       G. The wheel and the axle must decrease the work by half.

       H. The axle must stay still while the wheel turns.

       J. The wheel must have a fixed fulcrum.

_____ **11.** Four scouts are doing different jobs at camp. Which scout is using a pulley?

       A. Lizbeth pries open a can of fruit for breakfast.

       B. Sara rolls a wheelbarrow of firewood to the campsite.

       C. Katie raises the flag on the flagpole.

       D. Tonya trims hedges with hedge clippers.

_____ **12.** A wedge is a simple machine. What other kind of simple machine do you need to make a wedge?

       F. fulcrum   **H.** pulley

       G. inclined plane   **J.** screw

_____ **13.** Look at the labeled parts of the diagram.

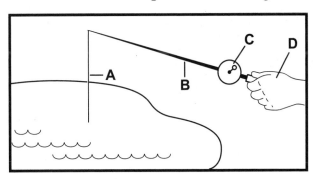

    Which part shows a fulcrum?

       A. Part A   **C.** Part C

       B. Part B   **D.** Part D

_____ **14.** Which simple machine is shown in the diagram?

       F. inclined plane   **H.** pulley

       G. lever   **J.** wedge

Name _____

____ **15.** Which of the following does **not** change the direction of a force?

 A. inclined plane   **C.** wedge

 B. pulley   **D.** wheel-and-axle

____ **16.** Screws have threads that are simple machines. What kind of machine are the threads on screws?

 F. blades   **H.** inclined planes

 G. fulcrums   **J.** wedges

Inquiry Skills

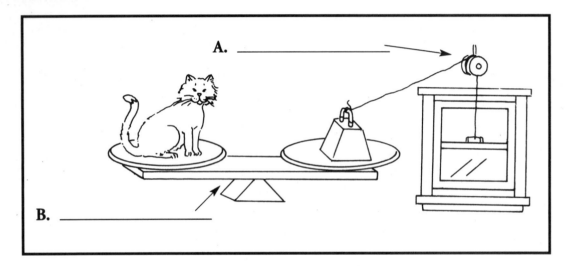

17. Label the simple machines in this **model** of a compound machine.

18. What do you **predict** will happen to the window if the cat jumps off the balance?

_____

_____

_____

Name _____

Critical Thinking

19. Builders are working together to put shingles on a roof. They need to get the shingles to the house and up to the roof. They also have to pry off the old shingles before putting on the new ones. What simple machines could they use to help them? Explain how they should use the machines.

_____

_____

_____

_____

_____

20. Suppose you want to use pulleys to send a message across a room.

Part A Devise a system using pulleys that you could use to deliver messages. Describe your system, and list the materials you would use to make it.

_____

_____

_____

_____

_____

Part B Explain how the pulleys allow you to do work.

_____

_____

Name _____

Date _____

Carrying Books

Materials

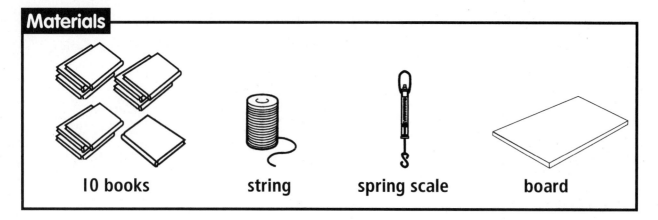

10 books   string   spring scale   board

Procedure

1 Tie three books tightly together with string. Leave enough string to attach to the spring scale.

2 Stack the other seven books in a pile.

3 Tie the end of the string to the spring scale. Use the scale to lift the three books to the top of the stack. Record the force in the space provided in the chart your teacher gives you.

4 Repeat the measurement two more times, and record the force. Calculate and record the average of the three measurements.

5 Place one end of the board on the floor, and place the other end of the board on top of the stack of seven books, forming a ramp.

6 Use the spring scale to pull the three books up the ramp to the top of the stack. Record the force in the chart.

7 Repeat the measurement two more times, and record the force. Calculate and record the average of the three measurements.

8 Which was the easier way to lift the three books to the top of the stack? Did this match what you thought would happen? Explain why or why not.

© Harcourt

Carrying Books

Materials   Performance Task sheet, 10 books, string, spring scale, board

Time   30 minutes

Suggested Grouping   pairs or small groups; alternatively, you can do the experiment yourself as a demonstration, with students helping you make and record measurements

Inquiry Skills   compare, measure, record, observe

Preparation Hints   Make a chart to record the findings on the three trials. Give a copy to each group. Include the column headings *Experiment 1 Force* and *Experiment 2 Force* and row headings *Trial 1, Trial 2, Trial 3,* and *Average.* Experiment with boards of different lengths and different numbers of books beforehand to ensure that the force readings will show a difference between the two methods.

Introduce the Task   Show students the experiment's setup by arranging a stack of books with and without a board. Point to the setup with the board, and ask students to identify the simple machine. (inclined plane) Have students make a prediction by asking them, **If I wanted to place more books on this stack, would it be easier to lift them to the top or to slide them to the top on the inclined plane?**

Promote Discussion   Discuss results with students, and ask whether their conclusions match their predictions. Ask what their results show about doing work with an inclined plane.

Scoring Rubric

Performance Indicators

_____ Constructs an inclined plane using books and a board.

_____ Measures accurately with a spring scale and correctly calculates averages.

_____ Concludes that it requires less force to move an object up an inclined plane than it does to lift an object straight up.

_____ Compares results to predictions.

Observations and Rubric Score

3	2	1	0

Write the letter of the best choice.

_____ **1.** Which of these is a device that opens or closes a circuit?

    A. charge

    B. conductor

    C. insulator

    D. switch

_____ **2.** Which materials can an electric current not flow through easily?

    F. circuits   **H.** insulators

    G. conductors   **J.** switches

_____ **3.** How are magnetic poles similar to electrical charges?

    A. Both have an N pole and an S pole.

    B. Both are poor conductors of electricity.

    C. When two are pulled apart, they may produce sparks.

    D. Opposite ones attract, and like ones repel.

_____ **4.** Which device changes electric energy into mechanical energy?

    F. electromagnet   **H.** motor

    G. generator   **J.** turbine

_____ **5.** Which of these is an example of something that has potential energy?

    A. fried eggs

    B. jet airplane as it flies

    C. pot of boiling water

    D. stretched rubber band

_____ **6.** What form of energy makes batteries work?

    F. chemical   **H.** geothermal

    G. electrical   **J.** mechanical

© Harcourt

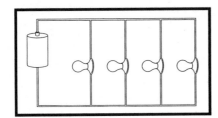

_____ **7.** What kind of circuit is shown in the picture above?

    A. mechanical

    B. parallel

    C. series

    D. static

_____ **8.** What is the speed of an object that travels 360 kilometers in 6 hours?

    F. 10 km/hr

    G. 30 km/hr

    H. 36 km/hr

    J. 60 km/hr

_____ **9.** When your bicycle speeds up, slows down, or changes direction, what is happening?

    A. acceleration

    B. gravitation

    C. inertia

    D. velocity

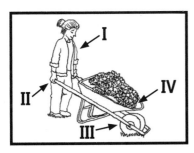

_____ **10.** Where is the fulcrum located in the drawing above?

    F. I   **H.** III

    G. II   **J.** IV

Name _____

____ **11.** Why do running shoes have rubber soles?
  A. to add weight
  B. to create inertia
  C. to increase friction
  D. to decrease velocity

____ **12.** When you weigh yourself, what are you actually measuring?
  F. particle motion   **H.** temperature
  G. gravitational force   **J.** volume

____ **13.** Which of the following is an example of work?
  A. doing a mental calculation   **C.** picking up a puppy
  B. observing an animal   **D.** reading a science lesson

____ **14.** What type of machine is used to open a window blind?
  F. inclined plane
  G. lever
  H. pulley
  J. wheel-and-axle

____ **15.** If you unwrapped the threads curled around a screw, which machine would you have?
  A. inclined plane   **C.** pulley
  B. lever   **D.** wedge

____ **16.** Which machine would you use to split wood?
  F. inclined plane   **H.** pulley
  G. lever   **J.** wedge

____ **17.** What is anything that changes the way work is done?
  A. force
  B. fulcrum
  C. machine
  D. motion

Name _____

_____ **18.** Which property of matter keeps it moving in a straight line?

     F. energy   **H.** magnetism

     G. inertia   **J.** mass

_____ **19.** What is produced by the kinetic energy of falling water?

     A. geothermal energy   **C.** chemical energy

     B. hydroelectric power   **D.** solar power

Write the answer to each question.

20. What are three examples of simple machines? How do they make work easier?

_____

_____

_____

21. Suppose you plug in a string of electric lights. If the lights are in a series circuit, what happens if one light goes out? Why? What happens if a light goes out in a parallel circuit? Why?

_____

_____

_____

_____

22. In a compound machine, two or more simple machines work together. Name two compound machines. Which simple machines make up each compound machine?

_____

_____

_____

Name _____

23. Speed tells you how an object's position changes during a certain amount of time. Answer the questions in Part A and Part B to calculate the speed of certain objects.

Part A What do you need to measure to find an object's speed? What is the formula for finding the speed of an object?

_____

_____

_____

Part B Suppose the Miller family, the Jones family, and the Edwards family are driving separately to meet at a favorite vacation place. Use the information below to determine the speed of each car. Complete the table. Remember to use the formula for finding speed and to show your work.

Family	Distance Traveled	Time Traveled	Speed
Miller	180 kilometers	3 hours	
Jones	300 kilometers	4 hours	
Edwards	210 kilometers	3 hours	

_____

_____

_____

_____

Page 1

Name _____

Date _____

Getting Ready for Science

Vocabulary 4 points each

Match each term in Column B with its meaning in Column A.

Column A

C **1.** An accepted measurement

F **2.** The set of steps scientists follow to find out how things work and affect each other

D **3.** An untested conclusion based on observations

B **4.** A tool with several lenses that can magnify an object many times

A **5.** A statement of what you think will happen in an experiment and why

E **6.** A set of steps designed to test a specific hypothesis

Column B

A. hypothesis

B. microscope

C. standard measure

D. inference

E. experiment

F. scientific method

Science Concepts 5 points each

Write the letter of the best choice.

C **7.** Which tool would you use to measure the pull of gravity on an object?
A. meterstick   **C.** spring scale
B. pan balance   **D.** thermometer

H **8.** What must you do before making an inference?
F. classify   **H.** observe
G. communicate   **J.** predict

Page 2

Name _____

D **9.** What are you doing when you use your knowledge to guess what will happen next?
A. comparing   **C.** observing
B. formulating   **D.** predicting

J **10.** A small box is 10 cm long, 5 cm wide, and 5 cm high. What is the volume of the box?

F. 20 cubic centimeters   **H.** 155 cubic centimeters
G. 55 cubic centimeters   **J.** 250 cubic centimeters

A **11.** Which tool would you use to measure the volume of a liquid?
A. beaker
B. forceps
C. pan balance
D. spring scale

J **12.** In which of these is a prediction made?
F. a dinner menu
G. a video game
H. a volcanic eruption
J. a weather forecast

A **13.** When you describe ways things are alike and ways they are different, which inquiry skill do you use?
A. compare
B. conclude
C. order
D. predict

Page 3

Name _____

G **14.** Look at the experimental setup below.

What information would this experiment give?
F. the effects of light on plant growth
G. the effects of soil on plant growth
H. the effects of air on plant growth
J. the effects of water on plant growth

D **15.** What must be controlled in an experiment?
A. classifications   **C.** graphs and tables
B. conclusions   **D.** variables

F **16.** What are scientists doing when they share the results of their investigations?
F. communicating   **H.** planning
G. experimenting   **J.** testing

B **17.** What does a pan balance measure?
A. force   **C.** motion
B. mass   **D.** volume

J **18.** What is usually the first step in the scientific method?
F. Conduct an experiment.
G. Draw conclusions.
H. Communicate results.
J. Observe and ask questions.

Page 4

Name _____

Critical Thinking 8 points each

19. A team of students is building a motorized vehicle for a science competition. The students do not yet know how they want to build the vehicle or what materials they need. What can the students do to save time and money before they start to build their vehicle?

Possible answer: The students can make a model. This will help them decide how to build the vehicle and identify the type and amount of materials they need.

20. Tyrone is carrying out an experiment to determine whether rainwater drains more quickly through soil made mostly of sand or soil made mostly of clay. The diagram below shows how he has set up his experiment.

Part A What variable does Tyrone want to test?
Tyrone wants to test the variable of soil type.

Part B Has Tyrone set up his experiment correctly? Explain.
No; Tyrone should have used an equal amount of each type of soil.

Unit A • Chapter I

Date _____

Chapter Assessment

Classifying Living Things

Vocabulary 4 points each

Match each term in Column B with its meaning in Column A.

	Column A		Column B
A	1. Probably the oldest living organisms		**A.** bacteria
G	2. Having tubes or channels		**B.** invertebrate
H	3. An animal with a backbone		**C.** microscopic
D	4. Without tubes or channels		**D.** nonvascular
E	5. A living thing		**E.** organism
B	6. An animal without a backbone		**F.** protists
F	7. Algae and protozoans		**G.** vascular
C	8. Too small to be seen with the eye alone		**H.** vertebrate

Science Concepts 4 points each

Write the letter of the best choice.

A 9. What are the building blocks of life?
- **A.** cells
- **B.** chloroplasts
- **C.** diatoms
- **D.** organisms

H 10. What controls all the functions of a cell?
- **F.** the cell membrane
- **G.** vacuoles
- **H.** the nucleus
- **J.** the nuclear membrane

B 11. What are the most numerous organisms on Earth?
- **A.** algae
- **B.** bacteria
- **C.** cells
- **D.** fungi

J 12. What kind of plant is shown in the picture?
- **F.** hornwort
- **G.** moss
- **H.** nonvascular
- **J.** vascular

D 13. How are humans classified?
- **A.** as invertebrates and amphibians
- **B.** as invertebrates and fish
- **C.** as vertebrates and reptiles
- **D.** as vertebrates and mammals

J 14. Why are the plants in the pictures classified as nonvascular?

- **F.** They reproduce by seeds.
- **G.** They reproduce by spores.
- **H.** They grow in damp forests and along riverbanks.
- **J.** They lack tubes for carrying water and food.

A 15. How are the cells of bacteria different from all other cells?
- **A.** They do not have a nucleus.
- **B.** They do not have a cell membrane.
- **C.** They are microscopic organisms.
- **D.** They are multicelled organisms.

H 16. Look at the pictures that Amy's teacher drew on the board. She asked the class to find something that all of these creatures have in common. What do you think they have in common?
- **F.** They are all insects.
- **G.** They are all arachnids.
- **H.** They are all arthropods.
- **J.** They are all crustaceans.

Inquiry Skills 8 points each

17. Sue wants to make and **use models** to compare vascular and nonvascular plants. To make one model, she wraps green modeling clay around long, thin straws. To this she attaches plant parts of different shapes. To make the other model, she takes a green toothpick and breaks it in half. She glues small pieces of green sponge along the sides of the toothpick. At the bottom of the toothpick, she glues small, thin pieces of white sponge. Which model is the vascular plant and which is the nonvascular plant? Explain.

The first model is the vascular plant; the straws represent the tubes that carry water and food. The second model is the nonvascular plant; it is much smaller and has no tubes to carry water and food.

18. Eduardo **observes** an organism with purple tubelike branches rooted to the floor of an aquarium. Eduardo **infers** that the organism is an animal, not a plant. Give a reason he might have made this inference.

Possible answers: The organism isn't green, so it might not make its own food; the branches are tubelike, possibly for filtering food.

Critical Thinking 10 points each

19. Some bacteria cause disease, but not all bacteria are harmful. List two ways in which bacteria are helpful.

Possible answers: They help us digest our food; they are used to help clean up oil spills; they make oxygen.

20. Dawn found this drawing of a plant. She has figured out that it's a vascular plant, but she can't determine the kind of vascular plant it is. Use what you know about plant classification to help her.

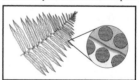

Part A What kind of vascular plant is shown here? Explain how you know.

It is a fern; the spores on the undersides of the leaves help identify it.

Part B Dawn is surprised that this plant does not show any signs of budding or of producing a flower. You are not surprised at this. Explain why not.

Not all vascular plants are flowering plants. There are two categories of vascular plants that do not produce flowers: cone-bearing plants and ferns. Since this plant is a fern, it does not produce flowers.

© Harcourt

Unit A • Chapter 2

Name _____
Date _____

Life Cycles

Vocabulary 4 points each

Match each term in Column B with its meaning in Column A.

Column A

B 1. The basic unit of heredity

A 2. A growth process in which an animal gets larger without going through major changes in body form

D 3. All the stages an organism goes through

F 4. A characteristic that makes one organism different from another

E 5. A growth process in which an animal goes through major changes in body form over the course of the life cycle

C 6. Processes by which characteristics pass from parents to offspring

Column B

A. direct development

B. gene

C. heredity

D. life cycle

E. metamorphosis

F. trait

Science Concepts 4 points each

Write the letter of the best choice.

D 7. What carries instructions for your growth and development?
A. your acquired traits   C. your family tree
B. your inherited traits   D. your genes

H 8. Where do an offspring's genes come from?
F. The mother contributes all of the genes.
G. The father contributes all of the genes.
H. Each parent contributes half of the genes.
J. Neither parent contributes any genes.

Unit A • Chapter 2   (page 1 of 4)   Assessment Guide   **AG 7**

Name _____

B 9. Which of these traits is determined **only** by heredity?
A. body size   C. intelligence
B. eye color   D. strength

G 10. After its birth, which animal is most likely to survive and thrive without receiving care from one or both parents?
F. a bird   H. a kitten
G. a fish   J. a seal

C 11. Which part of a plant feeds the embryo until the plant can make its own food?
A. the fruit   C. the seed
B. the roots   D. the stem

F 12. How do ferns and mosses reproduce?
F. from spores   H. through pollination
G. from seeds   J. by sending out runners

B 13. Which of these grow from storage stems called tubers?
A. ferns   C. strawberries
B. potatoes   D. trees, including apple trees

G 14. How do most animals begin the life cycle?
F. as a chrysalis   H. as a marsupial
G. as a fertilized egg   J. as a nymph

C 15. Which process does the picture show?

A. hatching
B. laying eggs
C. molting
D. reproducing

AG 8   Assessment Guide   (page 2 of 4)   Unit A • Chapter 2

Name _____

J 16. Which kind of animal goes through direct development?
F. a frog   H. a moth
G. a grasshopper   J. a spider

Inquiry Skills 8 points each

17. Jorge has planted some bean seeds in potting soil in clay pots and set the pots on a sunny window ledge. Write a **hypothesis** related to which plant part Jorge will **observe** first—the bean pods or the leaves. Explain why you think your hypothesis is correct.

Possible answer: The leaves will appear before the bean pods. The plant needs to make its own food and grow to a large size before it can produce flowers that, after pollination, make bean pods and seeds.

18. Write *1, 2, 3,* and *4* to indicate the correct **order** of development in this animal's life cycle. What kind of development do the pictures show? Explain.

Order: 2, 1, 4, 3. The pictures show an animal that undergoes complete metamorphosis, because the adult looks very different from the young.

Unit A • Chapter 2   (page 3 of 4)   Assessment Guide   **AG 9**

Name _____

Critical Thinking 10 points each

19. Describe the life cycle of the sea horse. What is unique about the sea horse's life cycle?

Possible answer: The female sea horse lays eggs in the male's pouch. The eggs are fertilized. After several weeks, baby sea horses come out of the pouch and swim away. Sea horses are unique because the male carries the babies.

20. Study the pictures. Use them to compare two plant life cycles.

I   II

Part A Which plant produces seeds, and which plant produces spores? Use the letters to identify the seeds and spores in the pictures.

The plant in I (the pea plant) produces seeds; b and c show the seeds. The plant in II (the fern) produces spores; g shows the spores.

Part B Which plant life cycle (I or II) includes two separate generations that each produce reproductive cells? Identify the generations by their letters in the picture. What other plants have similar life cycles?

Plant life cycle II; the separate generations, or stages, are f (which produces spores) and h (which produces sperm and eggs). Mosses have similar life cycles.

AG 10   Assessment Guide   (page 4 of 4)   Unit A • Chapter 2

Answer Key   (page 3 of 26)   **Assessment Guide   AG 135**

Unit A • Chapter 3

Name _____
Date _____

Adaptations

Vocabulary 4 points each

Match each term in Column B with its meaning in Column A.

Column A

_F_ **1.** An inherited behavior that helps an animal meet its needs

_E_ **2.** Evidence of a plant or an animal that lived a long time ago

_B_ **3.** A dormant, inactive state in which normal body activities slow

_H_ **4.** What happens when all members of a species die out

_A_ **5.** A body part or behavior that helps something live

_G_ **6.** Animals moving as a group from one region to another and back

_C_ **7.** Food, water, air, and shelter

_D_ **8.** Behaviors that were taught to an animal and help it meet its needs

Column B

A. adaptation

B. hibernation

C. basic needs

D. learned behaviors

E. fossil

F. instinct

G. migration

H. extinction

Science Concepts 4 points each

Write the letter of the best choice.

_B_ **9.** Which basic need do plants meet by themselves, if they have sunlight?
- **A.** air
- **B.** food
- **C.** shelter
- **D.** water

Name _____

_H_ **10.** Which is an example of a learned behavior?
- **F.** breathing
- **H.** reading
- **G.** eating
- **J.** sleeping

_D_ **11.** Which organism has fossils that show it has changed little over time?
- **A.** camel
- **C.** dinosaur
- **B.** corn
- **D.** turtle

_H_ **12.** A woodchuck has just gone into hibernation. Which is most likely to happen?
- **F.** It sleeps all summer.
- **G.** Its body temperature goes up.
- **H.** Its body temperature goes down.
- **J.** It stops breathing.

_B_ **13.** Which organism is **not** extinct?
- **A.** auk
- **C.** saber-toothed cat
- **B.** ginkgo
- **D.** woolly mammoth

_G_ **14.** Horses' teeth are adapted for which activity?
- **F.** eating meat
- **H.** eating both meat and plants
- **G.** chewing grasses
- **J.** cracking open seeds

_B_ **15.** David watches the birds that come to his backyard feeder. In the winter, there are few birds. In the spring, David makes a chart of which birds arrive first. Why might some bird species arrive at David's backyard feeder sooner than others?
- **A.** The early birds have a longer distance to travel.
- **B.** The early birds have a shorter distance to travel.
- **C.** The late birds didn't know what season it was.
- **D.** The late birds got lost on the way back.

Name _____

_J_ **16.** A tree falls and rots on the forest floor. The next year, new trees begin to grow in that spot. What is this an example of?
- **F.** the dead tree growing again
- **G.** people planting trees
- **H.** pollution
- **J.** the cycle of life

Inquiry Skills 8 points each

17. An ecosystem that you regularly **observe** has changed. You notice the animal populations shrinking. There are fewer plants. **Draw conclusions** about why the animal populations are shrinking.

Possible answer: The animal populations are either moving out or dying. They are doing this because their basic needs cannot be met by the habitat. There are fewer plants, so animals that feed on plants cannot find enough food. The plant populations may be shrinking because there is not enough water or one of their other basic needs can no longer be met.

18. You **observe** a mother cat washing her kittens. When the kittens are older, you **observe** them washing themselves. But you see that kittens without a mother wash themselves less often. What can you **infer** about the kittens' washing behavior?

The mother helps the kittens develop washing behavior.

Name _____

Critical Thinking 10 points each

19. The picture shows trees in stages of a cycle. Describe each stage, and explain why it is important.

Possible answer: Seeds are important because they grow into new trees. Adult trees are important because they provide shade, wood, and fruit. Decaying dead trees are important because they return nutrients to the soil for new trees to use.

20. Scientists can compare the fossils of prehistoric crocodiles with modern crocodiles to see how these animals have adapted over time.

Part A What are two things that fossil footprints of crocodiles tell scientists?
how big prehistoric crocodiles were and how they moved

Part B Look at the graph. It compares the sizes of extinct crocodiles and modern crocodiles. What difference do you see? Why do you think there is such a difference?

The graph shows that crocodiles have gotten smaller over time. The crocodiles became smaller as they adapted to changes in their environment.

Unit A • Chapter 4

Name _____
Date _____

The Human Body

Vocabulary 4 points each

Match each term in Column B with its meaning in Column A.

Column A　　　　　　　　　　　　**Column B**

B 1. A hard organ made of three kinds of tissue　　A. artery

F 2. An organ made of bundles of fibers　　B. bone

A 3. A blood vessel that carries blood away from the heart　　C. capillary

D. diaphragm

H 4. A blood vessel that carries blood back to the heart　　E. esophagus

G 5. The liquid in which blood cells travel　　F. muscle

E 6. A muscular tube that connects the mouth to the stomach　　G. plasma

H. vein

C 7. A tiny, thin-walled blood vessel

D 8. Muscle that causes breathing

Science Concepts 4 points each

Write the letter of the best choice.

A 9. Where do bones meet?
- A. joints
- B. ligaments
- C. tendons
- D. veins

Unit A • Chapter 4　　(page 1 of 4)　　Assessment Guide　**AG 19**

Name _____

G 10. Bones fit together in different ways. Where is there a ball and socket joint in your body?
- F. head
- G. shoulder
- H. knee
- I. neck

B 11. What kind of muscles make up the walls of the heart?
- A. capillary
- B. cardiac
- C. smooth
- D. skeletal

H 12. In which tube does air travel from your nose or mouth toward the lungs?
- F. artery
- G. capillary
- H. trachea
- I. vein

B 13. Muscles work to move bones back and forth. At least how many muscles work together to move one bone?
- A. 1
- B. 2
- C. 3
- D. 4

H 14. What is the name of the stringy tissues that connect bones together?
- F. capillaries
- G. joints
- H. ligaments
- I. tendons

B 15. Where does digestion in your body begin?
- A. esophagus
- B. mouth
- C. small intestine
- D. stomach

G 16. Stella is preparing a report about human skeletons. Which item should **not** be in her report?
- F. The skeleton helps us move.
- G. The skeleton helps us digest our food.
- H. The skeleton protects the organs inside our bodies.
- I. The skeleton supports our bodies and gives them shape.

AG 20　Assessment Guide　　(page 2 of 4)　　Unit A • Chapter 4

Name _____

Inquiry Skills 8 points each

17. Blood moves through your blood vessels and travels all over your body. But sometimes its movement is restricted. **Plan a simple investigation** to find out what happens when your blood is blocked inside a blood vessel. Use a length of tubing, such as a rubber hose, to represent your blood vessels and running water from the tap to represent your blood flow. Write down the steps you would follow.

Possible answer: First, I would get a hose, some water, and a marble. Then I would put the marble in the hose to create a blockage. Next I would attach the hose to a water source and turn on the water. I would observe what happened to the hose and the marble and write down my observations.

18. You have done an experiment modeling how quickly different foods would be digested in the stomach. Now it is time to prepare your report and **display the data** you have collected. You have information about the length of time each food took to dissolve and the names of five different kinds of food. What would be the best way to share your data with other members of your class?

Possible answer: I would create a bar graph of the different foods and how long they took to dissolve. I would clearly label the parts of my graph so that my classmates would be able to understand the information.

Unit A • Chapter 4　　(page 3 of 4)　　Assessment Guide　**AG 21**

Name _____

Read/Inquire/Explain 10 points each

19. Blood is pumped from the heart to the body and then back to the heart. Use the words *arteries, capillaries, heart,* and *veins* to show the path the blood takes through your body.

Student's answers should indicate that the blood flows from the heart, through the arteries, through the capillaries, through the veins and back to the heart.

20. In order to move blood through the body a pumping action must take place in the heart. The blood then moves through blood vessels to the lungs and the body.

Part A Look at the picture. One vessel is labeled with an X. What kind of vessel is this?

Vessel X is an artery, because the arrows show that it is carrying blood away from the heart.

Part B Where is the blood in vessel X going? Explain your answer.

The blood is flowing to the lungs. The blood returning from the body must go to the lungs to get oxygen before it can be pumped to the body.

AG 22　Assessment Guide　　(page 4 of 4)　　Unit A • Chapter 4

Unit A

Name _____

Date _____

Write the letter of the best choice. 4 points each

__C__ 1. Which part of a cell is responsible for activities that release energy?
  A. cell membrane
  B. chloroplast
  C. mitochondria
  D. nucleus

__H__ 2. What characteristic is used for grouping bacteria?
  F. function   H. shape
  G. movement   J. size

__B__ 3. Which part of a plant makes food and gives off oxygen?
  A. flowers   C. root
  B. leaves   D. stem

__F__ 4. What is the green coloring used in the process of photosynthesis?
  F. chlorophyll   H. spores
  G. chloroplast   J. starch

__A__ 5. What is the largest group of invertebrates?
  A. arthropods
  B. crustaceans
  C. insects
  D. worms

__F__ 6. How does water move in a bryophyte?
  F. from cell to cell
  G. from leaves to flowers
  H. from roots to stems
  J. from roots to tubelike structures

__C__ 7. What is the basic unit of heredity?
  A. cell
  B. characteristic
  C. gene
  D. trait

Name _____

__H__ 8. What is the first stage in a plant's life cycle?
  F. flowering
  G. fruiting
  H. germination
  J. seedling

__A__ 9. How is a clone of a plant produced?
  A. asexual reproduction   C. sexual reproduction
  B. grafting   D. tubers

__H__ 10. What is shown in the picture below?

  F. molting
  G. direct development
  H. complete metamorphosis
  J. incomplete metamorphosis

__D__ 11. What is shown in the picture below?

  A. molting
  B. direct development
  C. complete metamorphosis
  D. incomplete metamorphosis

__H__ 12. Which mammal does not fully develop inside the mother's body?
  F. cat   H. kangaroo
  G. dog   J. wolf

Name _____

__C__ 13. Which of these animals is ready to survive on its own when it is born?
  A. birds
  B. kangaroos
  C. reptiles
  D. dolphins

__F__ 14. What is a body part or a behavior that helps a living thing survive?
  F. adaptation
  G. basic need
  H. instinct
  J. nurture

__C__ 15. Which of these is an example of a living thing following an instinct?
  A. a baby learning to talk
  B. a child drawing a picture
  C. a dog barking at a stranger
  D. a horse responding to its trainer

__J__ 16. Which of these is **not** a reason animals might become extinct?
  F. an increase in predators
  G. a change in the habitat
  H. a decrease in the food supply
  J. a seasonal change in climate

__A__ 17. What do bears do to protect themselves during the winter months?
  A. hibernate
  B. hunt food
  C. migrate
  D. travel in herds

__H__ 18. What do hibernation and migration have in common?
  F. They are decreases in body temperature.
  G. They are moves from one region to another.
  H. They are instincts that help animals meet their needs.
  J. They are learned behaviors that help animals survive.

Name _____

__D__ 19. What is done by both the stem and the roots of a plant?
  A. supporting the leaves
  B. holding the plant in the ground
  C. pollinating flowers
  D. transporting water and nutrients

Write the answer to each question. 6 points each

20. Compare fungi and plants. How are they alike? How are they different?
  Possible answer: Fungi and plants both can grow in soil and have cells with cell walls. Fungi differ from plants in that they don't have chloroplasts and therefore cannot make their own food.

21. Suppose an animal moves out of its natural habitat. What do you think might happen? Why?
  Possible answer: The animal might not survive. Animals develop adaptations for specific environments and these adaptations may harm rather than help them in a different environment.

22. How do scientists infer what animals from long ago looked like?
  Possible answer: They use fossils to make a model and compare the model with animals they know about.

Name _____

23. Look at the model of a food web below. Use this model to answer Part A and Part B.

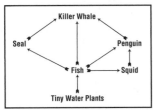

Killer Whale

Seal   Penguin

Fish   Squid

Tiny Water Plants

Part A Suppose the fish in this food web become sick and die. What might happen to all the animals that eat the fish?

Possible answer: The fish are food for most of the food web. Without fish to eat, the squid, penguin, and seal may die. Then the whales at the top of the web will not get enough food, and they may die.

Part B How might the loss of the fish affect the tiny water plants?

Possible answer: Fish eat the tiny water plants. If the fish die, there may be too many water plants. This might affect the habitat for the rest of the food chain.

Unit A   (page 5 of 5)   Assessment Guide **AG 29**

Chapter Assessment

Name _____
Date _____

Understanding Ecosystems

Vocabulary 4 points each

Match each term in Column B with its meaning in Column A.

Column A

F 1. All the living and nonliving things around us

E 2. The living and nonliving things in a particular place

B 3. Having to do with the living factors of an ecosystem

H 4. A group of the same kind of plant or animal, living in the same ecosystem

A 5. Work done to repair damaged ecosystems

G 6. Harmful substances mixed with water, air, or soil

C 7. All the groups of plants and animals living in the same ecosystem

D 8. Variety in living things

Column B

A. habitat restoration
B. biotic
C. community
D. diversity
E. ecosystem
F. environment
G. pollution
H. population

Science Concepts 4 points each

Write the letter of the best choice.

B 9. Which of these is **not** an example of a nonliving part of an ecosystem?
   A. air   **C.** water
   B. monkey   **D.** soil

H 10. Which is an example of an abiotic factor?
   F. insects   **H.** water
   G. plants   **J.** trees

AG 30 Assessment Guide   (page 1 of 4)   Unit B • Chapter 5

Name _____
Date _____

D 11. In which climate would ecosystems have the most diversity?
   A. desert   **C.** taiga
   B. savannah   **D.** tropical rain forest

H 12. The diagram shows two populations in a barn community. The cat population has just joined the barn community. Which is most likely to happen?

   F. mouse and cat populations both go up
   G. mouse and cat populations both go down
   H. mouse population goes down as cat population goes up
   J. mouse population goes up as cat population goes down

C 13. A landfill closes. The city covers the top with soil and then plants trees. What is this an example of?
   A. a biotic factor   **C.** habitat restoration
   B. erosion   **D.** pollution

G 14. Oil drips from cars onto a parking lot. Then rain washes it into a pond, where fish get sick and die. What is this an example of?
   F. adaptation   **H.** population
   G. pollution   **J.** restoration

Unit B • Chapter 5   (page 2 of 4)   Assessment Guide **AG 31**

Name _____

B 15. Meesha's lawn is an ecosystem. It includes grass, soil, air, insects, earthworms, and birds. Meesha puts extra water and fertilizer on her lawn. Which parts of the ecosystem will change?
   A. none
   B. all parts, because everything in an ecosystem interacts
   C. just the soil, because she's making it moister and richer
   D. just the grass, because that's why she's adding water and fertilizer

J 16. Bittersweet vines grow quickly up trees, where they block light and cause the trees to die. What is this an example of?
   F. trees meeting a basic need
   G. climate changing a population
   H. pollution harming an ecosystem
   J. a biotic factor changing an ecosystem

Inquiry Skills 8 points each

17. **Compare and contrast** the energy resources used by a car and a bicycle and the effects that a car and a bicycle have on an ecosystem.

Possible answer: A car uses gasoline, a fuel that cannot be replaced, while a bicycle uses a fuel that can be replaced (energy from food that you eat). A car gives off pollution, which hurts an ecosystem. Riding a bicycle does not give off any pollution and does not affect an ecosystem.

18. A highway crew clears the weeds off half of a hillside. After a rainstorm, the weedy part of the hill is the same, but most of the soil is washed away from the bare part. **Draw a conclusion** about the interaction of weeds and soil.

Possible answer: Weeds prevent soil erosion because their roots keep soil from washing away.

AG 32 Assessment Guide   (page 3 of 4)   Unit B • Chapter 5

© Harcourt

Name _____

Critical Thinking 10 points each

19. Describe steps that society can take to reduce air and water pollution.

Possible answer: People might put special devices on the tailpipes of their cars to control pollution. Factories could reduce the amount of chemicals they release into the air and not dump waste into rivers and streams.

20. Burrowing owls live in underground holes made by mammals such as prairie dogs. Burrowing owls eat mice, crickets, grasshoppers, and other small animals. Prairie dogs, mice, and grasshoppers all live in grasslands.

Part A What are two basic needs that burrowing owls can meet in a grassland, and how can they meet them?

The owls can find shelter in the prairie dog holes, and they can find food, such as mice and grasshoppers.

Part B The graph shows the populations of prairie dogs and burrowing owls in two pastures. Is there a relationship between the number of prairie dogs and the number of burrowing owls? Explain your answer, using information from the graph.

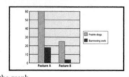

Possible answer: Pasture A has more prairie dogs than Pasture B. Pasture A also has more burrowing owls than Pasture B. So, the sizes of the two populations are directly related.

Chapter Assessment

Name _____
Date _____

Energy Transfer in Ecosystems

Vocabulary 4 points each

Match each term in Column B with its meaning in Column A.

Column A	Column B
G 1. Green plants, which make their own food	**A.** habitat
B 2. Animals, which cannot make their own food	**B.** consumers
E 3. Animals that eat only plants	**C.** decomposers
A 4. An environment that meets the needs of an organism	**D.** carnivores
F 5. Movement of food energy in a series of organisms	**E.** herbivores
C 6. Living things that feed on the wastes and remains of plants and animals	**F.** food chain
H 7. Consumers that eat prey	**G.** producers
D 8. Animals that eat only meat	**H.** predators

Science Concepts 4 points each

Write the letter of the best choice.

D 9. What is an environment that meets the needs of an organism?
  A. energy pyramid   **C.** food web
  B. food chain   **D.** habitat

G 10. From where does a first-level consumer get most of its energy?
  F. predators   **H.** second-level consumers
  G. producers   **J.** top-level consumers

Name _____

B 11. Which organism is **not** an omnivore?
  A. hyena   **C.** bear
  B. lion   **D.** human

H 12. Where do green plants get most of the energy they need to make their own food?
  F. carbon dioxide
  G. oxygen
  H. sunlight
  J. water

C 13. What is the term for the role that each living thing has in its habitat?
  A. food web   **C.** niche
  B. fossil   **D.** prey

G 14. Which animal is a carnivore?
  F. cow
  G. lion
  H. mouse
  J. rabbit

C 15. What is the term for food chains that overlap?
  A. consumer   **C.** food web
  B. extinction   **D.** producer

F 16. Miguel is writing a report about producers, consumers, herbivores, carnivores, and omnivores. Which of the following is a false statement that he should **not** include in his report?
  F. Producers eat consumers.
  G. Herbivores eat only plants, or producers.
  H. Omnivores eat both plants and other animals.
  J. Carnivores eat only other animals.

Name _____

Inquiry Skills 8 points each

17. How would you **compare** the diet of a carnivore to the diet of a herbivore?

Possible answer: A carnivore feeds only on other animals. Herbivores are animals that feed only on plants.

18. Joan saw a mushroom growing on the stump of a dead tree. What could Joan **infer** about the role of the mushroom?

Possible answer: The mushroom is a decomposer, feeding on the tree stump and breaking it down.

Critical Thinking 10 points each

19. The diagram shows a simple food chain. Which organism is the producer? Which organism is the first-level consumer? Explain.

grain   mouse   owl

The grain is the producer and the mouse is the first-level consumer. Plants make their own food and are producers. First-level consumers eat producers.

Name _____

20. The diagram shows how energy flows through an ecosystem.

```
                hawk

                foxes

                mice

                plants
```

Part A How does this diagram show that carnivores depend on green plants?

Possible answer: Herbivores eat green plants. Carnivores eat herbivores. If there were no green plants, there would be no herbivores and, therefore, no carnivores.

Part B Why are there fewer hawks and foxes than mice?

Possible answer: Only ten percent of the energy available to organisms at one level of the pyramid is passed to organisms at the next higher level. In the pyramid shown, there are not enough mice to support more foxes and hawks.

Unit B • Chapter 6   (page 4 of 4)   Assessment Guide   **AG 39**

Name _____
Date _____

Unit Assessment

Write the letter of the best choice. 4 points each

D 1. What is used often to name ecosystems?
   A. local rivers   C. the area's climate
   B. unusual plants   D. the main population

G 2. Which ecosystem has the largest number of different living things?
   F. desert   H. swamp
   G. rain forest   J. tundra

D 3. How is the Everglades like all communities?
   A. There are 43 kinds of mosquitoes.
   B. There are many rivers and swamps.
   C. The climate stays warm and wet all year.
   D. The plants and animals depend on each other.

G 4. Which of these is a biotic factor?
   F. air   H. sunlight
   G. plants   J. water

D 5. Which of these is an abiotic factor?
   A. earthworms   C. plants
   B. mosquitoes   D. soil

F 6. What are you observing when you record the amounts of rainfall and sunlight and the temperature of a region?
   F. climate   H. surroundings
   G. environment   J. population

B 7. Which of these is **not** a basic need of living things?
   A. food   C. shelter
   B. plants   D. water

H 8. What happens when bodies of dead animals decay?
   F. Oxygen is added to the air.
   G. Oxygen is taken from the air.
   H. Nutrients are added to the soil.
   J. Nutrients are taken from the soil.

AG 42 Assessment Guide   (page 1 of 5)   Unit B

Name _____

C 9. How can people affect ecosystems in a positive way?
   A. by plowing land to plant crops
   B. by clearing land for a new house
   C. by planting a new tree in the yard
   D. by using chemicals to fertilize the lawn

H 10. Look at the following list. Which of these are renewable resources?

oil	water
air	sunlight
coal	minerals

   F. oil, air, minerals
   G. minerals, oil, coal
   H. sunlight, air, water
   J. water, sunlight, minerals

D 11. Where do 40 percent of the medicines we use today come from?
   A. animals   C. minerals
   B. bacteria   D. plants

G 12. What is a major cause of air pollution?
   F. the fertilizing of crops   H. the cleaning of drain pipes
   G. the burning of gasoline   J. the emptying of paint cans

A 13.

What do the organisms shown in the picture above have in common?
   A. They are all producers.
   B. They are all carnivores.
   C. They are all consumers.
   D. They are all decomposers.

Unit B   (page 2 of 5)   Assessment Guide   **AG 43**

Name _____

H 14. What type of consumer are you if you eat both plants and animals?
   F. carnivore   H. omnivore
   G. decomposer   J. producer

D 15. What does every food chain start with?
   A. consumers
   B. predators
   C. prey
   D. producers

G 16. How much energy is passed from one organism to another along a food chain?
   F. 3 percent   H. 70 percent
   G. 10 percent   J. 90 percent

A 17. What might have formed when a plant leaf fell on muddy ground millions of years ago?
   A. fossil   C. mineral deposit
   B. organism   D. petrified wood

G 18. What can scientists learn about an ancient animal from a fossil footprint?
   F. its age
   G. its size
   H. what color it was
   J. what food it ate

B 19. Look at the following food chain. Which of these is the producer?

   A. mouse   C. hawk
   B. grass   D. snake

AG 44 Assessment Guide   (page 3 of 5)   Unit B

© Harcourt

Name _____

Write the answer to each question. **6 points each**

20. What are three ways in which animals are adapted to survive the winter months? Explain each.

Possible answer: Some animals migrate, or move, to warmer climates for the winter months. Some animals hibernate. These animals can survive for long periods on a tiny bit of food and oxygen, because their heart and breathing rates slow almost to a stop. Some animals just sleep a lot during the winter months, but they still remain active. They are not hibernating.

21. Consumers can't make their own food, so they eat other living things. What are the three types of consumers? Explain and give an example of each.

Possible answer: Herbivores eat only plants. Horses, giraffes, squirrels, rabbits, and some people are herbivores. Carnivores eat only other animals. The panther and lion are carnivores. An omnivore eats both plants and animals. Bears, hyenas, and some people are omnivores.

22. What is a niche? How does it help living things and their habitats?

Possible answer: A niche is the way an organism interacts with its habitat, including how it gets food and shelter, reproduces, cares for its young, and avoids danger. Niches help maintain an ecosystem's balance. For example, predators' eating of prey helps control the prey's population.

Unit B   (page 4 of 5)   Assessment Guide   **AG 45**

Name _____

23. An ecosystem has both living and nonliving parts. Both parts are needed for an ecosystem to survive. Answer the questions in Part A and Part B to explain why this is true.

Part A How do plants and animals help each other in an ecosystem?

Possible answer: Plants provide food for some animals, including humans. Plants also provide shelter for some animals. People use wood from trees to build their homes. When animals eat plants, they stop the plants from spreading and taking over all the available space. Animal droppings make the soil richer, so plants grow better.

Part B What are the nonliving parts of an ecosystem? Why are they important to its survival?

Possible answer: The nonliving parts include sunlight, air, water, and soil. Animals and plants need the gases in air to survive. A change in water supply can cause plants to die and animals to find other homes or die. If the soil is poor, plants won't grow. Few plants mean few animals in an ecosystem. Air, water, and soil can contain harmful substances that can affect both plants and animals.

AG 46   Assessment Guide   (page 5 of 5)   Unit B

Name _____

Date _____

The Rock Cycle

Vocabulary 4 points each

Match each term in Column B with its meaning in Column A.

Column A	Column B
E **1.** The changing of rocks over time	**A.** weathering
G **2.** The bottom layer of soil	**B.** mineral
F **3.** A layer of soil	**C.** humus
B **4.** A solid substance that occurs naturally in rocks or in the ground	**D.** erosion
	E. rock cycle
H **5.** The type of rock that forms when melted rock cools and hardens	**F.** horizon
A **6.** The breaking down of Earth's surface into pieces	**G.** bedrock
	H. igneous
C **7.** The remains of decayed plants and animals	
D **8.** The process of moving sediment to other places	

Science Concepts 4 points each

Write the letter of the best choice.

D   **9.** Leon says that the soil in his garden feels rough. What physical property of soil is he observing?

   A. layers   **C.** shape

   B. luster   **D.** texture

G   **10.** Which substance makes up most of Earth's crust?

   F. humus   **H.** sediment

   G. rock   **J.** soil

Unit C • Chapter 7   (page 1 of 4)   Assessment Guide   **AG 47**

Name _____

B   **11.** What property do all soil horizons share?

   A. bottom layer of humus

   B. partly weathered rock

   C. same types of minerals

   D. upper layer of bedrock

J   **12.** Which property of minerals is being tested in the picture?

   F. luster

   G. hardness

   H. magnetism

   J. streak

A   **13.** Which of these processes does **not** contribute to the weathering and erosion that shapes landforms?

   A. pressure   **C.** waves

   B. plants   **D.** wind

G   **14.** Sometimes two of the plates that make up Earth's surface come together and push against each other. What new landforms may begin to develop as a result?

   F. glaciers

   G. mountains

   H. oceans

   J. sinkholes

B   **15.** Sinkholes occur occasionally in Florida. What causes sinkholes?

   A. Animals dig and move rocks.

   B. Water dissolves underground rock.

   C. Plants grow through cracks in rocks.

   D. Sediment is moved from one place to another.

AG 48   Assessment Guide   (page 2 of 4)   Unit C • Chapter 7

© Harcourt

Name _____

F **16.** Which layer of soil contains humus?
F. Layer F
G. Layer G
H. Layer H
J. Layer I

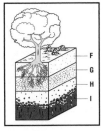

Inquiry Skills **8 points each**

17. You are studying soil samples. You have one with dark soil and one with light-colored rough soil. What can you **infer** about the origins of each?

Possible answer: A place with a lot of humus, such as a forest, produces a dark soil. A light-colored soil may have formed in a place, such as a desert, where there is little plant life to contribute to humus.

18. **Compare** rocks and minerals. How are they alike? How are they different?

Possible answer: Alike: Both are solid substances found in nature. Different: A mineral occurs naturally in rocks or in the ground; rocks are made of one or many minerals. There are more than 4,000 minerals; rocks can be classified into three groups, depending on how they are formed.

Name _____

Critical Thinking **10 points each**

19. Rocks are classified into three groups. Name each group of rock, and tell how each type of rock is formed.

Possible answer: Igneous rocks form when melted rock cools and hardens. Sedimentary rocks form from sediment that has piled up in layers over time. Metamorphic rock is formed from any other rock by heat and pressure.

20. Miners traveled deep into a mine in search of gold. They found lots of smooth, small stones and some shiny gold rocks.

Part A To tell whether the shiny rocks were gold or pyrite (fool's gold), the miners decided to do a streak test. Describe a streak test, and explain how it would identify the rocks as gold or pyrite.

Possible answer: A streak test is done by rubbing a rock across a surface such as white tile. The color of the streak helps identify the mineral. Pyrite leaves a greenish-black streak, and gold leaves a golden streak.

Part B Explain what could have happened over the years to make the small stones in the mine smooth.

Possible answer: The stones are weathered rock. They could be pieces that broke off of big rocks. Perhaps there was once a river there and the stones were weathered by the moving water.

Name _____
Date _____

Chapter Assessment

Changes to Earth's Surface

Vocabulary **4 points each**

Match each term in Column B with its meaning in Column A.

Column A	Column B
H 1. A landform that forms where lava flows on Earth's surface	A. deposition
C 2. The remains or traces of an organism that lived long ago	B. earthquake
	C. fossil
G 3. The shape of landforms in an area	D. glacier
F 4. A landform much higher than the land around it	E. landform
D 5. A large, moving mass of ice	F. mountain
E 6. A natural feature of Earth's surface	G. topography
B 7. A shaking of Earth's surface	H. volcano
A 8. The dropping of soil and rock by rivers	

Science Concepts **4 points each**

Write the letter of the best choice.

C **9.** Which of these does a plain have?
A. deep valleys
B. highlands
C. mostly flat land
D. steep cliffs

Name _____

J **10.** How are deltas and dunes alike?
F. They both form along sandy coasts.
G. They both form at the ends of rivers.
H. The movement of fast-moving rivers forms both.
J. The movement of sand and sediment forms both.

B **11.** Why does Earth's inner core remain solid?
A. It is almost as hot as the sun.
B. The pressure on it is very great.
C. The heat around it is very great.
D. It is made mostly of iron and nickel.

F **12.** Which of Earth's layers includes the land that makes up the continents and the land under the oceans?
F. crust   H. inner core
G. mantle   J. outer core

A **13.** Where do most earthquakes occur?
A. along faults
B. in Earth's core
C. on valley floors
D. near coastal plains

H **14.** What would you find in the upper parts of Earth's mantle?
F. fertile soil   H. melted rock
G. iron and nickel J. solid rock

D **15.** What causes a tree to become petrified?
A. The tree is preserved in sap.
B. Glaciers cause the tree to freeze.
C. Sediment forms around the tree.
D. The tree's wood is replaced by rock.

© Harcourt

Name _____

<u>J</u> **16.** Suppose you are a scientist observing this fossil. What might you learn about the animal that made these tracks?

F. where it might have lived

G. what foods it might have eaten

H. what sounds it might have made

J. how big it might have been

A   B

17. Observe each diagram carefully. Which one shows a possible shield volcano? How can you tell? Which diagram shows a possible cinder cone volcano? How can you tell?

Diagram A shows a shield volcano. I can tell because it has gently sloping sides. Diagram B shows a cinder cone volcano because it has steep sides and it is shooting chunks of rock into the air.

18. Imagine that Earth's plates have stopped moving. **Predict** what Earth's surface will look like a few million years in the future.

Possible answer: There will be no new mountain ranges, and eventually everything will become flat because of weathering and erosion.

Unit C • Chapter 8   (page 3 of 4)   Assessment Guide   **AG 55**

Name _____

19. Palm trees are usually found in warm climates. However, scientists have found fossils of palm trees in Wyoming. What can scientists infer from this fossil record?

Possible answer: Scientists might infer that Wyoming's climate must have been much warmer long ago.

20. The picture shows the active volcanoes in the Pacific Ocean Basin. This group of volcanoes is called the Ring of Fire.

Part A Why is this a good name for this group of volcanoes?

Possible answer: The Ring of Fire is a good name because the volcanoes circle, or make a ring around, the Pacific Ocean.

Part B How do you think these volcanoes form?

Possible answer: The plates moving toward each other result in the edges of one plate being pushed down into the mantle, which causes the plate above it to melt. Magma rises through vents all around the edges of the Pacific Plate, forming the volcanoes.

AG 56   Assessment Guide   (page 4 of 4)   Unit C • Chapter 8

Name _____

Date _____

Write the letter of the best choice. **4 points each**

<u>C</u> **1.** What do scientists examine to tell minerals apart?

A. rock cycle

B. soil horizons

C. physical properties

D. chemical weathering

<u>J</u> **2.** Which of these rocks is formed from other types of rocks by heat and pressure?

F. igneous   H. sedimentary

G. andesite   J. metamorphic

<u>D</u> **3.** Which happens when you rub a mineral across a surface?

A. The mineral cuts the surface.

B. The mineral magnetizes the surface.

C. The mineral breaks apart.

D. The mineral leaves a streak.

<u>H</u> **4.** What is the classification of rocks based on?

F. their color   H. how they form

G. their shape   J. how they heat and cool

<u>B</u> **5.** What is the sequence of processes that change rock over long periods?

A. erosion

B. rock cycle

C. weathering

D. mountain building

<u>H</u> **6.** What causes most weathering?

F. heat

G. ice

H. water

J. wind

Unit C   (page 1 of 5)   Assessment Guide   **AG 59**

Name _____

<u>A</u> **7.** Which of these is **not** a cause of erosion?

A. heat

B. ice

C. water

D. wind

<u>H</u> **8.** What makes up the largest part of soil?

F. air

G. humus

H. sediment

J. water

<u>A</u> **9.** What substance forms the hard underlying layer of Earth's surface?

A. bedrock   C. sand

B. clay   D. sediment

<u>F</u> **10.** What determines soil type and soil color?

F. the area where the soil forms

G. different types of organisms

H. the composition of soil horizons

J. varying amounts of sand, silt, and clay

<u>B</u> **11.** What makes soil horizons different from each other?

A. layers of topsoil

B. particles of different size

C. areas of weathered rock

D. amounts of water and air

<u>H</u> **12.** Where do dunes form?

F. in valleys   H. along sandy coasts

G. on mountains   J. at the ends of rivers

AG 60   Assessment Guide   (page 2 of 5)   Unit C

Name _____

A 13. Which landform is shown in the picture below?

    A. canyon
    B. delta
    C. island
    D. valley

G 14. What are you observing when you look at the shape of landforms in an area?
    F. deposition   **H.** fossil records
    G. topography   **J.** Earth's mantle

B 15. What happens when two plates along a fault shift quickly?
    A. A volcano erupts.
    B. An earthquake occurs.
    C. A barrier island forms.
    D. A mountain range arises.

G 16. Where do most fossils form?
    F. on ice sheets   **H.** in open spaces
    G. in sedimentary rock   **J.** beside petrified wood

B 17. What is the main source of clues about Earth's past life and environment?
    A. trace fossils   **C.** fossil footprints
    B. fossil record   **D.** geologic time scale

© Harcourt

Name _____

J 18. What new landform may form when two plates push into each other?
    F. delta
    G. dune
    H. island
    J. mountain

B 19. When did dinosaurs live?
    A. Cenozoic Era   **C.** Paleozoic Era
    B. Mesozoic Era   **D.** Precambrian Era

Write the answer to each question. **6 points each**

20. What can scientists learn from studying fossils?
    Possible answer: They can learn about plants and animals from long ago. They can also tell how these plants and animals changed over time. They can tell about an animal's size or how it moved from a fossil footprint. Fossils of animal droppings show what an animal ate.

21. What happens during a river's deposition?
    Possible answer: Bits of soil and rock carried and deposited by rivers build landforms such as deltas and floodplains.

© Harcourt

Name _____

22. How can living things cause weathering?
    Possible answer: As they grow, plant roots wedge into and split the rocks around them. Digging animals move rocks closer to Earth's surface, where rainwater can reach them.

23. Use the following drawing to answer Parts A and B.

Part A Identify the layers of Earth in the drawing above.
    A—crust, B—mantle, C—outer core, D—inner core

Part B What might you find in each layer?
    Possible answer: The crust includes the land that makes up the continents and the land under the oceans. The mantle is the rock layer below the crust. The upper parts of the mantle contain magma. The crust and upper mantle are broken into large slabs of rock called plates. The core is made mostly of iron and nickel. The outer core is liquid. The inner core is solid.

© Harcourt

Chapter Assessment

Name _____
Date _____

The Water Cycle

Vocabulary **4 points each**

Match each term in Column B with its meaning in Column A.

	Column A	Column B
C	1. Instrument that measures air pressure	**A.** air mass
G	2. Process in which water moves from the surface of Earth to the air and then back again	**B.** anemometer
H	3. Process by which a gas changes into a liquid	**C.** barometer
A	4. Large body of air	**D.** hurricane
D	5. Tropical storm with wind speeds of 119 km/hr (74 mi/hr) or more	**E.** precipitation
F	6. Process by which a liquid changes into a gas	**F.** evaporation
B	7. Instrument that measures wind speed	**G.** water cycle
E	8. Water that falls back to Earth	**H.** condensation

Science Concepts **4 points each**

Write the letter of the best choice.

B 9. Of the following temperatures, which is the lowest at which liquid rain is likely to fall?
    A. 0° C   **C.** 16° C
    B. 7° C   **D.** 23° C

J 10. Sonya listens to daily weather forecasts because she is hoping for a snowy day. Which of these weather changes might bring snow?
    F. warm, dry air masses   **H.** cold, dry air masses
    G. warm, wet air masses   **J.** cold, wet air masses

© Harcourt

Name _____

B **11.** Where do most storms form?
   A. over land   **C.** in the "eye"
   B. at fronts   **D.** over a peninsula

F **12.** What might happen when two air masses come together and form a warm front?
   F. steady rain
   G. thunderstorms
   H. a strong sea breeze
   J. cooler temperatures

A **13.** John is showing his class how liquid water can be changed to other forms. What will happen when he heats the liquid water to a high temperature?
   A. It will evaporate.
   B. It will condense.
   C. It will form clouds.
   D. It will attract dust particles.

J **14.** Jenny is looking at a drawing of one of the steps in the water cycle. Which of the following describes this step?

   F. Water vapor rises into the air.
   G. Water vapor is changed to a gas.
   H. Water vapor is warmed by the sun.
   J. Water vapor becomes precipitation.

Name _____

A **15.** Which of these causes flooding during a hurricane?
   A. rain and storm surge   **C.** clouds of a thunderstorm
   B. the "eye" of a storm   **D.** spirals of high winds

J **16.** You and your friend are planning a trip to the beach. Your friend does not like walking on hot sand, but he does like swimming in warm water. What time of the day might be the best for you and your friend to visit the beach?
   F. 12:00 P.M.   **H.** 4:00 P.M.
   G. 2:00 P.M.   **J.** 6:00 P.M.

Inquiry Skills 8 points each

17. The most accurate way to describe weather is to use data from weather instruments. Name three weather instruments you might choose to **measure** the weather, and tell what each measures.
   Possible answers: Thermometers measure temperature, and barometers measure air pressure. Rain gauges measure rainfall amounts, and wind vanes measure wind direction. Anemometers measure wind speed.

18. Design **models** of two simple weather instruments you could make. Explain how your weather instruments work.
   Possible answers: a measuring container for collecting rainwater left outdoors for a period of time; a weather vane using a dowel and pinwheel with direction markings to be observed on windy days

---

Name _____

Critical Thinking 10 points each

19. Think about what happens to water when it falls on land. Explain how rain that falls in your community eventually might end up in an ocean.
   Possible answer: When the ground cannot hold more water, the groundwater becomes runoff and flows into creeks and streams. It then flows into rivers and, eventually, into oceans.

20. Strong sea breeze storms happen often in Florida during the summer. These storms frequently form over the center of the peninsula.

Part A   Explain how a sea breeze forms.
   Possible answer: During the day, the air over water is cooler than the air over land. The hot air over the land is pushed upward by the cool air over the water as it moves inland. This causes a sea breeze.

Part B   Why do you think these storms form over the center of Florida?
   Possible answer: Florida is surrounded by water on three sides. Sea breezes can come in from the east and from the west. When these breezes meet, the air becomes very unstable. If the air masses have a lot of water vapor, a very strong sea breeze storm could form over the center of the peninsula.

Chapter Assessment

Name _____
Date _____

Planets and Other Objects in Space

Vocabulary 4 points each

Match each term in Column B with its meaning in Column A.

	Column A	Column B
G	**1.** The star at the center of our solar system	**A.** axis
C	**2.** A small planet-like body that orbits Earth	**B.** galaxy
E	**3.** A large object that orbits a star	**C.** moon
F	**4.** A huge burning ball of superheated gas	**D.** orbit
B	**5.** A large system of stars, gas, and dust	**E.** planet
H	**6.** Everything that exists in space	**F.** star
D	**7.** Earth's path as it moves around the sun	**G.** sun
A	**8.** An imaginary line that goes through both poles of a planet	**H.** universe

Science Concepts 4 points each

Write the letter of the best choice.

C **9.** Kevin is describing the way the moon appears to change shape. What term should he use to describe the different shapes of the moon?
   A. comets   **C.** phases
   B. constellations   **D.** satellites

H **10.** How long does it take Earth to rotate once around its axis?
   F. 1 hour   **H.** 1 day
   G. 12 hours   **J.** 1 year

© Harcourt

Name _____

C **11.** Alana saw a full moon last night. In two weeks, what will she see?

A. C.

B. D.

H **12.** Willa is preparing a report about the outer planets. Which planet should she include in her report?
  F. Mars   H. Saturn
  G. Mercury   J. Venus

B **13.** Which two gases make up most of the sun?
  A. oxygen and helium   C. hydrogen and oxygen
  B. helium and hydrogen   D. oxygen and carbon dioxide

F **14.** What is one reason that seasons change?
  F. Earth is tilted on its axis.
  G. Earth rotates on its axis.
  H. The sun moves around the Earth.
  J. The temperature of the sun changes.

B **15.** Mark is wondering why Mars is called the Red Planet. What would you tell him?
  A. All the inner planets are red.
  B. Mars looks fiery red from Earth.
  C. Mars is surrounded by burning gases.
  D. Mars is the closest planet to the sun.

Name _____

F **16.** What does a star's color tell us about the star?
  F. how hot it is
  G. how far away it is
  H. whether it has planets orbiting it
  J. whether it is in the Milky Way galaxy

Inquiry Skills **8 points each**

17. Will is **making a model** of the solar system **using numbers.** He found this information about the planets.

Planet	Diameter (kilometers)	Planet	Diameter (kilometers)
Mercury	4,800	Saturn	120,000
Venus	12,000	Uranus	52,000
Earth	12,800	Neptune	49,500
Mars	6,700	Pluto*	2,300
Jupiter	143,000		

*a "dwarf planet"

Which planets will be the largest and smallest parts of his model?

Largest: Jupiter; smallest: Pluto

18. It is summer in the Northern Hemisphere. The average temperature in Miami is 28°C. The average temperature in Seattle is 18°C. How do these **measurements** help show the effect of Earth's tilt on its axis?

Possible answer: Miami is farther south than Seattle. Because of Earth's tilt on its axis, the sun's rays don't hit Seattle as directly as they do Miami. So, the temperature won't be as high in Seattle as in Miami.

Name _____

Critical Thinking **10 points each**

19. Every four years, the year has 366 days instead of the normal 365 days. Why is it necessary to have a year with 366 days every four years?

Possible answer: It takes Earth about $365\frac{1}{4}$ days to revolve around the sun (one year). Every four years the extra $\frac{1}{4}$ days add up to one full day, so that year is a leap year with 366 days. If we didn't have leap years, the calendar would eventually be off by many days.

20. The positions of the constellations seem to change with the season. For example, in the Northern Hemisphere we see Orion during the winter.

Part A Can people in the Southern Hemisphere see Orion when we see it? Explain your answer.

Possible answer: No. People in the Southern Hemisphere are facing a different part of space than we are, so they cannot see Orion.

Part B Explain why the stars seem to change position as the seasons change.

Possible answer: As Earth orbits the sun, we see different parts of space at different times of the year.

Unit Assessment

Name _____
Date _____

Write the letter of the best choice. **4 points each**

A **1.** What forms when water vapor cools and condenses on dust particles in the air?
  A. clouds
  B. precipitation
  C. rain shadow
  D. water vapor

J **2.** Which form of precipitation occurs when water vapor turns directly into ice?
  F. hail   H. sleet
  G. rain   J. snow

D **3.** What is a fast-spinning spiral of wind that stretches from the clouds of a thunderstorm to the ground?
  A. hurricane   C. thunderstorm
  B. storm surge   D. tornado

F **4.** Why do strong sea-breeze storms occur often in Florida?
  F. Most of Florida is a peninsula.
  G. Most of Florida has a rain shadow.
  H. Florida has many land breezes.
  J. Florida is a barrier island.

B **5.** What causes changes in the weather?
  A. moisture level of an air mass
  B. movement of an air mass
  C. separation of an air mass
  D. temperature of an air mass

J **6.** What causes the water cycle to continually occur?
  F. evaporation   H. stationary fronts
  G. condensation   J. the sun's energy

© Harcourt

Name _____

Use the drawing below to answer Questions 7–8.

B 7. In the drawing above, a warm air mass is colliding with a cold air mass. What is the border between the two air masses called?
- **A.** eye
- **B.** front
- **C.** rain shadow
- **D.** thunderstorm

H 8. What kind of weather is likely to occur if the warm air mass moves over the cold air mass?
- **F.** hail
- **G.** snow
- **H.** steady rain
- **J.** thunderstorm

D 9. Which picture shows the phases of the moon in the correct order?

F 10. What might be the result if a tropical storm grew stronger?
- **F.** hurricane
- **G.** sea-breeze storm
- **H.** tornado
- **J.** warm front

Unit D   (page 2 of 5)   Assessment Guide   AG 77

Name _____

C 11. What separates the inner planets and the outer planets?
- **A.** gas giants
- **B.** fiery comets
- **C.** ring of asteroids
- **D.** moons with rings

F 12. Which of these is **not** an inner planet?
- **F.** Jupiter   **H.** Mercury
- **G.** Mars   **J.** Venus

C 13. About how often does the pattern of moon phases repeat?
- **A.** $11\frac{1}{2}$ days   **C.** $29\frac{1}{2}$ days
- **B.** 24 hours   **D.** 365 days

H 14. Which planet was the last to be discovered by scientists?
- **F.** Earth   **H.** Pluto
- **G.** Mars   **J.** Uranus

D 15. What is the star in the center of our solar system?
- **A.** moon
- **B.** comet
- **C.** universe
- **D.** sun

H 16. What is the smallest planet in the solar system?
- **F.** Mars
- **G.** Neptune
- **H.** Pluto
- **J.** Venus

D 17. Which of these is a huge ball of superheated gas?
- **A.** asteroid   **C.** moon
- **B.** comet   **D.** star

AG 78   Assessment Guide   (page 3 of 5)   Unit D

Name _____

F 18. Which of these is in the correct order from smallest to largest?
- **F.** constellation, galaxy, universe   **H.** universe, galaxy, constellation
- **G.** galaxy, universe, constellation   **J.** galaxy, constellation, universe

C 19. What can you learn about stars from their color?
- **A.** how old they are   **C.** how hot or cool they are
- **B.** how far away they are   **D.** how small or large they are

Write the answer to each question. 6 points each

20. Why does the moon seem to have different shapes, or phases?

Possible answer: It takes a little more than 28 days for the moon to orbit Earth. The moon's light is reflected from the sun. As the moon orbits Earth, different amounts of its lit surface can be seen. The phases of the moon follow the same pattern about every 28 days.

21. Where does the information on a weather map come from?

Possible answer: Information is collected at weather stations across the country. This information is then reported to the National Weather Service (NWS). The NWS makes daily weather maps based on this information.

22. Why is Earth considered the most unusual inner planet?

Possible answer: Earth is the only planet to have liquid surface water and a large amount of oxygen in the atmosphere. The water and oxygen support life on Earth.

Unit D   (page 4 of 5)   Assessment Guide   AG 79

Name _____

23. Use the following drawing to answer Part A and Part B. Choose from the following terms to answer Part A: evaporation, condensation, precipitation.

Part A What is happening at Point A? What is happening at Point B? What is happening at Point C?

Point A—precipitation (rain); Point B—condensation (cloud formation); Point C—evaporation

Part B What happens during the process of evaporation? Give an example. What happens during the process of condensation? Give an example.

Possible answer: In evaporation, a liquid changes into a gas. A large amount of water evaporates from oceans, lakes, and rivers every day. Water also evaporates from the soil, puddles, and your skin. Condensation is the process in which a gas changes into a liquid. Water dripping from an air conditioner is water vapor that condensed when it cooled. Condensed water and dust particles form clouds.

AG 80   Assessment Guide   (page 5 of 5)   Unit D

Unit E • Chapter 11

Chapter Assessment

Name _____

Date _____

Matter and Its Properties

Vocabulary 4 points each

Match each term in Column B with its meaning in Column A.

Column A

D 1. Everything that takes up space

C 2. The amount of matter something contains

H 3. The amount of space that matter takes up

E 4. Two or more substances that are combined without changing any of them

G 5. A measure of how much material will dissolve in another kind of matter

A 6. The amount of matter compared to the volume

F 7. Matter that has a definite shape and volume

B 8. Matter that has no definite shape and takes up no definite amount of space

Column B

A. density

B. gas

C. mass

D. matter

E. mixture

F. solid

G. solubility

H. volume

Science Concepts 4 points each

Write the letter of the best choice.

A 9. What affects the boiling point of water?
A. altitude
B. density
C. volume
D. weight

Unit E • Chapter 11   (page 1 of 4)   Assessment Guide   **AG 81**

Name _____

G 10. Which animal would probably have the most mass?

F.   H.

G.   J.

A 11. Which of the following is **not** a state of matter?
A. density
B. gas
C. liquid
D. solid

J 12. Lori is stirring some salt into water. What is she making?
F. a gas
G. solubility
H. matter
J. a solution

D 13. Kim is making a surprise gift. She needs material of a definite size and shape. Which state of matter must the material be in?
A. gas   C. mixture
B. liquid   D. solid

F 14. Raphael is grouping different kinds of matter together. Which group contains **only** examples of matter?
F. garbage, gate, grape, grass
G. hair, heat, hip bone, horse
H. leg, lemon, light, lung
J. sand, soil, sound, sugar

AG 82   Assessment Guide   (page 2 of 4)   Unit E • Chapter 11

Name _____

D 15. Which has the greatest solubility in water?
A. oil
B. paper
C. sand
D. sugar

H 16. Jorge wants to show that physical properties can be used to tell different foods apart. What physical property would be most useful to tell the difference between mint ice cream and spinach?
F. color
G. mass
H. taste
J. volume

Inquiry Skills 8 points each

17. **Compare** the densities below by arranging the substances from least dense to most dense.

Aluminum: 2.7   Gold: 19.3   Iron: 7.9   Lead: 11.3   Silver: 10.5   Water: 1.0

water, aluminum, iron, silver, lead, gold

18. Gladys poured sugar into a glass of water and stirred the solution. In time, no more sugar dissolved. Gladys then heated the solution and added more sugar. The extra sugar dissolved. What can Gladys **infer** about the effect of heating on the solubility of sugar in water?

Students' answers should indicate that as the temperature increases, the solubility of sugar in water also increases.

Unit E • Chapter 11   (page 3 of 4)   Assessment Guide   **AG 83**

Name _____

Critical Thinking 10 points each

19. A diagram of particles of water in the liquid state would show that the particles can move freely past one another. For water in the gas state, a diagram would show that the particles are spread apart and have even greater movement. What would a diagram of particles of water in the solid state show?

Students' answers should indicate that the water molecules in the solid state would be in a tight, evenly spaced pattern.

20. The graphs at the right show the effect of temperature on the solubilities of two substances.

Part A What happens to the solubility of substance A as the temperature increases?

As the temperature increases, the solubility of substance A also increases.

Part B Do both substances behave in the same way as the temperature increases? Explain your answer.

Both substances do not behave in the same way. The solubility of substance A increases as the temperature increases. The solubility of substance B decreases as the temperature increases.

AG 84   Assessment Guide   (page 4 of 4)   Unit E • Chapter 11

© Harcourt

Unit E • Chapter 12

Name _____
Date _____

Changes in Matter

Vocabulary 4 points each

Match each term in Column B with its meaning in Column A.

Column A

D 1. A physical change that occurs when matter changes from one state to another

A 2. The smallest possible particle of an element

H 3. A property that involves how a substance interacts with other substances

C 4. A substance made of just one kind of atom

E 5. A change that results in the formation of new substances

B 6. A substance made of two or more kinds of atoms that are chemically combined

F 7. A trait of a substance by itself

G 8. A change that does not result in a new substance

Column B

A. atom

B. compound

C. element

D. change of state

E. chemical change

F. physical property

G. physical change

H. chemical property

Science Concepts 4 points each

Write the letter of the best choice.

C 9. Which of these is matter?
- A. energy
- B. light
- C. paper
- D. sound

Name _____

J 10. Eric has samples of iron, gold, silver, and steel. Which of these is **not** an element?
- F. iron
- G. gold
- H. silver
- J. steel

D 11. Which of these describes a chemical property of a substance?
- A. colorless
- B. odorless
- C. a liquid at 20°C
- D. reacts with oxygen

F 12. Which of the following is a chemical reaction?
- F. Hydrogen and oxygen combine to form water.
- G. Liquid water freezes and becomes ice.
- H. A rock is crushed into small pieces.
- J. Sugar dissolves in hot tea.

A 13. Saundra heated water until it became a gas. Which term identifies this change?
- A. boiling
- B. condensing
- C. freezing
- D. melting

G 14. Which is a common physical property of nonmetals?
- F. They are shiny.
- G. They are brittle.
- H. They can be stretched out thin.
- J. They can be drawn out into wires.

A 15. Which is **not** a compound?
- A. oxygen
- B. salt
- C. sulfur dioxide
- D. water

Name _____

H 16. Elena made this chart about water.

Boiling point:	100°C
Melting point:	0°C
Odor:	none
Color:	none

Which is the best title for Elena's chart?
- F. How Water Is Formed
- G. Chemical Properties of Water
- H. Physical Properties of Water
- J. Chemical Reactions of Water

Inquiry Skills 8 points each

17. A chemist heats a white solid. When the temperature reaches 52°C, the white solid melts and turns into a liquid. **Predict** what will happen when the liquid cools below 52°C.

   Possible answer: The liquid will turn back into a solid as it reaches its freezing point.

18. Darci has some metal shavings that are attracted to a magnet. Darci mixes the metal shavings with a yellow powder. She then separates the metal shavings from the powder by using the magnet. **Draw a conclusion** about whether a chemical reaction has taken place.

   Possible answer: No, because the metal shavings can still be separated from the yellow powder by using a magnet. The properties of the metal remain the same; the metal did not react with the yellow powder to form a new substance.

Critical Thinking 10 points each

19. Jason dissolved a big spoonful of salt in a glass of water. How can Jason show that the salt has gone through a physical change and not a chemical change? Explain.

   Jason can show that the salt has gone through a physical change by allowing all the water to evaporate. The salt will remain at the bottom of the glass. If the salt had gone through a chemical change, it would not still be salt.

20. Faith places an iron nail in each of two bottles. She adds water to Bottle 1. Then she closes both bottles. After several days, she notices that rust has formed on the nail in Bottle 1.

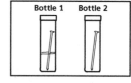

Bottle 1   Bottle 2

Part A Why did rust form on the nail in Bottle 1?

   Possible answer: Iron rusts when both oxygen and water are present. Faith added water to the bottle. The oxygen came from the air inside the bottle.

Part B Why did the iron nail in Bottle 2 not have any rust?

   Possible answer: The nail in Bottle 2 was exposed to oxygen in the air, but not to water. (Some students may note that the air in Bottle 2 contained water vapor, but that the amount of water wasn't sufficient to cause the iron to rust.)

© Harcourt

Unit E • Chapter 13

Name _____

Date _____

Chapter Assessment

Sound

Vocabulary 4 points each

Use the terms below to complete the sentences.

absorption	frequency	reflection	vibration
amplitude	pitch	transmission	wavelength

1. A quick back-and-forth motion is a _____**vibration**_____

2. _____**Pitch**_____ is how high or low a sound is.

3. To find out how loud or soft a sound is, you measure its _____**amplitude**_____

4. The distance from a point on one wave to the same point on another wave is the _____**wavelength**_____

5. When you measure the number of waves that pass in a second, you find the _____**frequency**_____

6. A wave's bouncing off a surface is called _____**reflection**_____

7. _____**Absorption**_____ stops sound waves from reflecting or traveling any farther.

8. _____**Transmission**_____ means that sound waves keep moving through materials to produce sound.

Unit E • Chapter 13   (page 1 of 4)   **Assessment Guide**   **AG 93**

Name _____

Science Concepts 4 points each

Write the letter of the best choice.

A 9. Which unit is used to measure the loudness of common sounds?
- **A.** decibel
- **B.** electrical signals
- **C.** oscilloscope
- **D.** wavelength

F 10. Which kind of sound is produced by sound waves with peaks that are very close together?
- **F.** high
- **G.** loud
- **H.** low
- **J.** soft

A 11. While hiking, Claud calls his friend's name loudly. What might he hear when the sound waves bounce off the smooth surface of a cliff?
- **A.** an echo
- **B.** silence
- **C.** a jumble of sounds
- **D.** his friend's response

J 12. Which part of the ear acts as a funnel for sound waves?
- **F.** cochlea
- **G.** eardrum
- **H.** hammer, anvil, and stirrup
- **J.** outer ear

C 13. Sound waves cause which part of the ear to vibrate first?
- **A.** bones
- **B.** cochlea
- **C.** eardrum
- **D.** hammer, anvil, and stirrup

F 14. In which part of the ear are vibrations changed to nerve signals?
- **F.** cochlea
- **G.** eardrum
- **H.** hammer, anvil, and stirrup
- **J.** outer ear

AG 94   Assessment Guide   (page 2 of 4)   Unit E • Chapter 13

Name _____

Use the graph below to answer Questions 15 and 16.

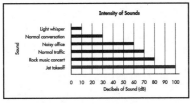

Intensity of Sounds

A 15. Which is softer than normal conversation?
- **A.** light whisper
- **B.** noisy office
- **C.** normal traffic
- **D.** rock music concert

F 16. Which is louder than a rock music concert?
- **F.** jet takeoff
- **G.** noisy office
- **H.** normal conversation
- **J.** normal traffic

Inquiry Skills 8 points each

17. While riding in a car, you notice that the wheels make sounds against the pavement. The pitch rises as the car speeds up. State a **hypothesis** based on this observation.

    The pitch of car wheels increases with speed because the vibrations caused by the wheels get faster as the car moves faster.

18. You want to **experiment** to test how well various materials muffle sounds. Which variables will you keep the same? Which variable will you change?

    Same: person listening, sound being blocked, room where test is made; Change: material blocking sounds

Unit E • Chapter 13   (page 3 of 4)   **Assessment Guide**   **AG 95**

Name _____

Critical Thinking 10 points each

19. Which instrument plays at a higher pitch? Why?

bass   violin

    The violin plays at a higher pitch. Its strings are shorter than those on the bass, so the sounds they produce are at a higher frequency.

20. Peyton is standing at her front door. Her friend Omar is five houses down the street. Peyton yells, "Omar!"

Part A How is the sound of Peyton's voice transmitted to Omar?

    The sound is transmitted by the vibrations of air molecules between Peyton and Omar.

Part B Omar doesn't hear Peyton when she calls. When she calls again, what are two things she can do to make sure Omar hears her?

    Possible answers (any two): Move closer to Omar so that the sound doesn't have to travel as far; yell louder; cup her hands around her mouth to direct the sound waves in Omar's direction.

AG 96   Assessment Guide   (page 4 of 4)   Unit E • Chapter 13

© Harcourt

Unit E • Chapter 14

Name _____

Date _____

Light and Heat

Vocabulary 4 points each

Match each term in Column B with its meaning in Column A.

Column A

D 1. A form of energy that can travel through space

F 2. Light bouncing off an object

A 3. Light bending when it changes speed

E 4. Heat that can't be used to do work

H 5. The way heat travels through materials that are touching

C 6. The movement of heat in liquids and gases

B 7. The movement of heat without matter

G 8. The change of energy from one form to another

Column B

A. refraction

B. radiation

C. convection

D. light

E. waste heat

F. reflection

G. energy transfer

H. conduction

Science Concepts 4 points each

Write the letter of the best choice.

A 9. Sasha pulls down a window shade to block the sunlight completely. Which word describes the window shade?
A. opaque
B. radiant
C. translucent
D. transparent

Name _____

F 10. Vahid places a pan on a hot electric stove burner. How does the burner heat the pan?
F. conduction
G. convection
H. radiation
J. reflection

B 11. All cups are full. Which cup has the most energy?
A. cup 1
B. cup 2
C. cup 3
D. Cup 1 and cup 2 have the same total energy.

F 12. What happens to light when it hits a mirror?
F. It reflects.   H. It is absorbed.
G. It refracts.   J. It passes through.

B 13. Which example of matter would carry heat by convection?
A. bread
B. lemonade
C. sand
D. seashells

J 14. When a thermometer is warmed, the liquid inside it rises. While this is happening, what is true about the particles of the liquid?
F. They move less.
G. They stop vibrating.
H. They move more slowly.
J. They have more energy.

Name _____

D 15. Emily is watching bread bake in an oven. The oven door is closed, but it is warm next to the oven. What is warming Emily?
A. reflection
B. refraction
C. solar power
D. waste heat

J 16. What does temperature measure?
F. heat in matter
G. heat absorbed by matter
H. total energy transferred by matter
J. average energy of particles in matter

Inquiry Skills 8 points each

17. An artist puts a piece of metal into a vat of water. The temperature of the water rises. What can you **infer** about the original temperature of the metal and the water?

When the metal was first put into the water, it was warmer than the water. The water temperature rose as heat was transferred from the metal to the water.

18. A turkey should be cooked until it is 86°C. An oven cooks a turkey by conduction. Where should you put a thermometer to **measure** whether the whole turkey is done cooking?

You should put the thermometer in the meat of the turkey. Placing it elsewhere will just measure the temperature of something other than the turkey itself.

Name _____

Critical Thinking 10 points each

19. Marisol and Anita are visiting the bookmobile. Marisol is standing in the sun. Anita is standing in the shade.

Which girl can see the sun? Explain.

Marisol can see the sun. Light travels in a straight line from the sun to her eyes, and there is nothing blocking her from the sun.

20. The picture shows two solar cookers. One is clean and shiny. The other is dirty and dull. Everything else about the cookers is the same.

Part A Which cooker will reach a higher temperature?
the clean, shiny cooker

Part B Explain why the cooker you chose will reach a higher temperature.
The shiny cooker reflects more light and heat, so there is more energy to raise the temperature in the middle.

Answer Key

© Harcourt

Unit E

Name _____

Date _____

Unit Assessment

Write the letter of the best choice. 4 points each

D 1. Which of these always takes up the same amount of space and keeps its shape?
  A. gas
  B. liquid
  C. matter
  D. solid

H 2. Which of these is **not** a physical property of matter?
  F. mass
  G. volume
  H. ability to burn
  J. ability to conduct heat

C 3. What is the result of the flowing of thermal energy from warmer to cooler objects?
  A. change of state
  B. electrical property
  C. heat
  D. temperature

F 4. An object has a mass of 16 grams and a volume of 4 cubic centimeters. What is its density?
  F. 4 g/cm^3
  G. 12 g/cm^3
  H. 20 g/cm^3
  J. 64 g/cm^3

B 5. Which of these substances is a liquid at –10°C?
  A. iron
  B. mercury
  C. oxygen
  D. water

F 6. What is the smallest possible particle of a substance?
  F. atom
  G. element
  H. grain
  J. matter

Unit E   (page 1 of 5)   Assessment Guide **AG 105**

Name _____

I   II   III   IV

B 7. Which of the objects pictured above contains material with a definite volume, but no definite shape?
  A. I
  B. II
  C. III
  D. IV

G 8. Which change of state occurs when a gas cools?
  F. boiling
  G. condensing
  H. freezing
  J. melting

A 9. Which of these involves a change of state that results in a new substance?
  A. burning wood
  B. carving stone
  C. dissolving sugar
  D. melting ice

H 10. Which of the following is a physical change?
  F. baking bread
  G. burning wood
  H. cutting an apple
  J. rusting iron

AG 106 Assessment Guide   (page 2 of 5)   Unit E

Name _____

A 11. Which of these involves a chemical change?
  A. baking bread
  B. boiling water
  C. cutting wood
  D. freezing water

H 12. Which of these is a clue that a chemical change is probably taking place?
  F. change in size
  G. change in state
  H. change in color
  J. change in shape

C 13. Which of these would produce a sound with a low pitch and loud intensity?
  A. baby crying
  B. child whispering
  C. large dog barking
  D. small dog barking

H 14. Which of these is **not** used to describe sound waves?
  F. amplitude
  G. frequency
  H. transverse
  J. wavelength

A 15. What happens to sound in a carpeted room?
  A. absorption
  B. reflection
  C. transmission
  D. vibration

F 16. Which of these materials is opaque?
  F. brick wall
  G. clear glass
  H. clear plastic
  J. wax paper

C 17. How is heat carried in an empty space, where there is no matter?
  A. conduction
  B. convection
  C. radiation
  D. thermal energy

Unit E   (page 3 of 5)   Assessment Guide **AG 107**

Name _____

H 18. Which use of heat makes changes in matter?
  F. bathing bodies
  G. heating homes
  H. melting metals
  J. washing clothes

C 19. What is Earth's main source of heat and light?
  A. gas
  B. oil
  C. sun
  D. wood

Write the answer to each question. 6 points each

20. When you shout down a long, narrow hall, why do you sometimes hear an echo?

  Possible answer: When sound waves strike a smooth surface, they are reflected back in the same pattern. You hear the sound again.

21. Why is your shadow behind you when you face the sunlight?

  Possible answer: You are blocking the path of some of the light. The dark area where the light is blocked is your shadow. Light travels in straight lines and does not go around corners. That's why the area behind you is dark and forms a shadow.

22. How can you prove that air has mass?

  Possible answer: You could use two of the same kind of ball, one that is inflated and one that is not. Use a scale to weigh each ball. The inflated ball weighs more. It has air in it. The extra mass has to come from the air inside the ball.

AG 108 Assessment Guide   (page 4 of 5)   Unit E

© Harcourt

Answer Key   (page 21 of 26)   **Assessment Guide** **AG 153**

Name _____

23. Use the data in the following table to answer Part A and Part B.

Process	Clue
1. chopping wood	logs or splinters
2. burning wood	ash; smell of smoke
3. frying eggs	becomes firm; color changes
4. shredding paper	thin strips

Part A Interpret the data in the table to infer whether a physical or a chemical change occurs in each process.

Process 1—physical change; Process 2—chemical change;

Process 3—chemical change; Process 4—physical change

Part B What happens to a substance during a physical change? What happens to a substance during a chemical change?

Possible answer: A physical change is a change that does

not result in a new substance. The substance changes to a

different form of the same thing. A chemical change results

in one or more new substances.

Name _____
Date _____

Making and Using Electricity

Vocabulary 4 points each

Match each term in Column B with its meaning in Column A.

Column A

__A__ 1. A material that lets electricity travel through it easily

__H__ 2. An electrical charge that builds up in an object

__E__ 3. An object that attracts iron

__B__ 4. A temporary magnet

__C__ 5. A machine that produces electric current

__F__ 6. The energy of motion

__D__ 7. A path that has more than one way an electric current can flow

__G__ 8. Energy an object has because of its position or condition

Column B

A. conductor
B. electromagnet
C. generator
D. parallel circuit
E. magnet
F. kinetic energy
G. potential energy
H. static electricity

Science Concepts 4 points each

Write the letter of the best choice.

__A__ 9. What is stored in the bonds that hold compounds together?
   A. chemical energy   **C.** magnets
   B. insulators   **D.** static electricity

__J__ 10. What kind of energy is also called energy of position?
   F. generator   **H.** motor
   G. kinetic   **J.** potential

Name _____

__D__ **11.** What is the name of a path that has only one way for the current to flow?
   A. current electricity
   B. magnetic field
   C. power field
   D. series circuit

battery
light bulb

__F__ **12.** Which is a good conductor of electricity?
   F. copper
   G. glass
   H. plastic
   J. rubber

__B__ **13.** Jack and his family visited a large dam, where they were told that the kinetic energy of falling water was changed to electrical energy. What kind of power did this dam produce?
   A. chemical power   **C.** geothermal power
   B. hydroelectric power   **D.** solar power

__F__ **14.** What is a stream of electrons moving through a copper wire called?
   F. current electricity
   G. generator
   H. magnetic field
   J. motor

__B__ **15.** Todd wants to build a small electric generator. What two items must he have to make his generator?
   A. coal and oil
   B. coil of wire and magnet
   C. steam and turbine
   D. wire and switch

Name _____

__J__ **16.** A magnet will hold papers to a refrigerator, but papers are not attracted to a magnet. What can be concluded about the refrigerator, the magnet, and the papers?
   F. The refrigerator, the magnet, and the papers are all magnetic.
   G. The refrigerator and the magnet become magnetized by the papers.
   H. Magnetic forces pass from the papers to both the refrigerator and the magnet.
   J. Magnetic forces pass from the magnet, through the papers, to the refrigerator.

Inquiry Skills 8 points each

17. Offices, homes, and factories each use about the same amount of electricity. If you made a pie graph to **compare** the amounts used, what fraction of the graph would be labeled for each kind of user?

Students' answers should indicate that each fraction would be

the same, one-third.

18. Suppose you are testing the strength of an electromagnet. You are changing the number of loops of wire. You are measuring how many paper clips the electromagnet can pick up. Describe a table that you would use to **record the data.**

Students should describe a two-column table with the

headings "Loops" and "Paper Clips Picked Up." Some

students may suggest a third column labeled "Other

Observations."

Name _____

Name _____

Date _____

Critical Thinking 10 points each

19. Batteries supply a stream of electrons to power toys and electronics. When some batteries wear out, they can be recharged. Explain how this might be possible.

Students' answers should indicate that electrons move from one place in a battery, through the toy or other device, to another place in the battery. The direction of electron flow is reversed to recharge a battery.

20. Electrical devices can be wired together in different ways.

Key
— battery
⊗ light bulb
‿— switch

Part A Figure A shows a circuit. When one light bulb is removed, the others stay lit. Is this a parallel circuit or a series circuit? Explain.

Possible answer: This is a parallel circuit. In a parallel circuit, there is more than one path for electrons to follow.

Part B Figure B shows a switch in an electrical circuit. Is the switch part of the circuit in a series connection or in a parallel connection? Explain.

Possible answer: The switch is wired in series. At the place where the switch is, there is no other path for the current to follow.

Unit F • Chapter 15   (page 4 of 4)   Assessment Guide   AG 113

Forces and Motion

Vocabulary 4 points each

Match each term in Column B with its meaning in Column A.

Column A

E 1. A force that acts between all masses and causes them to attract one another

G 2. The change of position during a unit of time

H 3. The speed and direction of an object

B 4. A push or a pull

C 5. The force of attraction between Earth and other objects

F 6. A force that resists motion, relative to each other, of objects that are touching

A 7. A change in speed or direction of an object's motion

D 8. The property of matter that keeps a moving object moving in a straight line

Column B

A. acceleration
B. force
C. gravity
D. inertia
E. gravitation
F. friction
G. speed
H. velocity

Science Concepts 4 points each

Write the letter of the best choice.

D 9. What is the measurement of the force of gravity on an object?
A. acceleration   **C.** speed
B. mass   **D.** weight

F 10. Which force resists motion between objects that are in contact?
F. friction   **H.** speed
G. mass   **J.** velocity

AG 116   Assessment Guide   (page 1 of 4)   Unit F • Chapter 16

Name _____

A 11. Which one of the following causes acceleration?
A. force
B. inertia
C. speed
D. weight

G 12. What is the least number of photographs needed to tell if a horse is moving?
F. 1
G. 2
H. 7
J. 100

D 13. Henri wants to explain what is meant by mass. How should he describe the mass of his body?
A. the weight of his body in newtons
B. the weight of his body in pounds
C. the volume occupied by his body
D. the amount of matter in his body

H 14. Which type of force causes a boy jumping off a chair to move toward Earth?
F. buoyant
G. electrical
H. gravitational
J. magnetic

B 15. What two things must Stephanie measure to find the speed of a moving bicycle?
A. mass and inertia
B. distance and time
C. gravity and friction
D. position and motion

Unit F • Chapter 16   (page 2 of 4)   Assessment Guide   AG 117

Name _____

G 16. After studying acceleration, Amos explains why the gas pedal in a car is called an accelerator. What should Amos say in his explanation?
F. An accelerator increases friction.
G. An accelerator causes a change in the car's velocity.
H. An accelerator balances the effect of gravitational force.
J. An accelerator is used to keep the velocity the same.

Inquiry Skills 8 points each

17. List the tools you need to **measure** speed. Tell how you would use them.

Students should list a tool to measure distance and a tool to measure time. To measure speed, measure the distance an object moves and the time it takes to travel the distance. Divide the distance by the time.

18. Suppose you are a scientist who has just finished an experiment to test the effects of friction on motion. What information about your experiment would you **communicate** to another scientist so that he or she could check your results?

Students' answers should include materials used, procedural steps, results, and any unusual or unexpected observations.

AG 118   Assessment Guide   (page 3 of 4)   Unit F • Chapter 16

Name _____

19. Margaret watched a magician pull a tablecloth out from under a set of dishes without moving the dishes. What property of matter was Margaret observing? Explain.

Students' answers should indicate that Margaret was observing the property of inertia. Inertia is the tendency of matter at rest to stay at rest.

20. Diagram A shows a 2-kilogram pillow and a 2-kilogram brick. Diagram B shows a 1-kilogram pillow and a 1-kilogram brick.

A   **B**

Part A Does the 2-kilogram pillow have twice as much mass as the 1-kilogram pillow? Explain.

Possible answer: Yes. The 2-kilogram pillow would contain twice as much matter as the 1-kilogram pillow.

Part B Where would the 1-kilogram pillow weigh half as much as the 2-kilogram brick?

Possible answer: The 1-kilogram pillow would weigh half as much as the 2-kilogram brick any time they were weighed in the same place.

Simple Machines

Match each term in Column B with its meaning in Column A.

		Column A	Column B
D	**1.**	A machine with few or no moving parts, to which only one force is applied	**A.** pulley
F	**2.**	Two inclined planes placed back to back	**B.** work
H	**3.**	The fixed point on a lever	**C.** inclined plane
B	**4.**	The use of force to move an object over a distance	**D.** simple machine
A	**5.**	A wheel with a line around it	**E.** lever
E	**6.**	A bar that pivots on a fixed point	**F.** wedge
G	**7.**	A post with threads wrapped around it	**G.** screw
C	**8.**	A slanted surface	**H.** fulcrum

B **9.** Scientists have a special meaning for *work*. Which one of these is an example of scientific work?
- **A.** pushing on a door that won't open
- **B.** lifting a box off the floor
- **C.** standing still with a backpack strapped to your back
- **D.** reading a textbook

Name _____

F **10.** What must a wheel and an axle do to be a simple machine?
- **F.** The wheel and the axle must turn together.
- **G.** The wheel and the axle must decrease the work by half.
- **H.** The axle must stay still while the wheel turns.
- **J.** The wheel must have a fixed fulcrum.

C **11.** Four scouts are doing different jobs at camp. Which scout is using a pulley?
- **A.** Lizbeth pries open a can of fruit for breakfast.
- **B.** Sara rolls a wheelbarrow of firewood to the campsite.
- **C.** Katie raises the flag on the flagpole.
- **D.** Tonya trims hedges with hedge clippers.

G **12.** A wedge is a simple machine. What other kind of simple machine do you need to make a wedge?
- **F.** fulcrum
- **G.** inclined plane
- **H.** pulley
- **J.** screw

D **13.** Look at the labeled parts of the diagram.

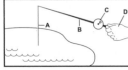

Which part shows a fulcrum?
- **A.** Part A
- **C.** Part C
- **B.** Part B
- **D.** Part D

G **14.** Which simple machine is shown in the diagram?
- **F.** inclined plane
- **G.** lever
- **H.** pulley
- **J.** wedge

Name _____

D **15.** Which of the following does **not** change the direction of a force?
- **A.** inclined plane
- **C.** wedge
- **B.** pulley
- **D.** wheel-and-axle

H **16.** Screws have threads that are simple machines. What kind of machine are the threads on screws?
- **F.** blades
- **H.** inclined planes
- **G.** fulcrums
- **J.** wedges

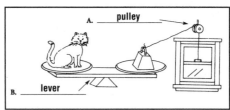

17. Label the simple machines in this **model** of a compound machine.

18. What do you **predict** will happen to the window if the cat jumps off the balance?

The right side of the balance will go down, the weight will pull on the string, and the window will open.

© Harcourt

Name _____

Critical Thinking **10 points each**

19. Builders are working together to put shingles on a roof. They need to get the shingles to the house and up to the roof. They also have to pry off the old shingles before putting on the new ones. What simple machines could they use to help them? Explain how they should use the machines.

   Possible answer: To pry off the shingles, they could use levers. To bring the shingles to the house, they could push a wheelbarrow up an inclined plane to their truck. A pulley could be used to lift the shingles to the roof.

20. Suppose you want to use pulleys to send a message across a room.

   Part A Devise a system using pulleys that you could use to deliver messages. Describe your system, and list the materials you would use to make it.

   Answers will vary, but most students will describe two pulleys being used for the message delivery. There is a string that moves over the two pulleys. The message could be clipped onto the string. The materials that are needed are two pulleys, string, and a clip.

   Part B Explain how the pulleys allow you to do work.

   Possible answer: The pulleys allow you to use force to move an object, a message.

Name _____
Date _____

Write the letter of the best choice. 4 points each

D 1. Which of these is a device that opens or closes a circuit?
   A. charge
   B. conductor
   C. insulator
   D. switch

H 2. Which materials can an electric current not flow through easily?
   F. circuits   H. insulators
   G. conductors   J. switches

D 3. How are magnetic poles similar to electrical charges?
   A. Both have an N pole and an S pole.
   B. Both are poor conductors of electricity.
   C. When two are pulled apart, they may produce sparks.
   D. Opposite ones attract, and like ones repel.

H 4. Which device changes electric energy into mechanical energy?
   F. electromagnet   H. motor
   G. generator   J. turbine

D 5. Which of these is an example of something that has potential energy?
   A. fried eggs
   B. jet airplane as it flies
   C. pot of boiling water
   D. stretched rubber band

F 6. What form of energy makes batteries work?
   F. chemical   H. geothermal
   G. electrical   J. mechanical

Name _____

B 7. What kind of circuit is shown in the picture above?
   A. mechanical
   B. parallel
   C. series
   D. static

J 8. What is the speed of an object that travels 360 kilometers in 6 hours?
   F. 10 km/hr
   G. 30 km/hr
   H. 36 km/hr
   J. 60 km/hr

A 9. When your bicycle speeds up, slows down, or changes direction, what is happening?
   A. acceleration
   B. gravitation
   C. inertia
   D. velocity

H 10. Where is the fulcrum located in the drawing above?
   F. I   H. III
   G. II   J. IV

Name _____

C 11. Why do running shoes have rubber soles?
   A. to add weight
   B. to create inertia
   C. to increase friction
   D. to decrease velocity

G 12. When you weigh yourself, what are you actually measuring?
   F. particle motion   H. temperature
   G. gravitational force   J. volume

C 13. Which of the following is an example of work?
   A. doing a mental calculation   C. picking up a puppy
   B. observing an animal   D. reading a science lesson

H 14. What type of machine is used to open a window blind?
   F. inclined plane
   G. lever
   H. pulley
   J. wheel-and-axle

A 15. If you unwrapped the threads curled around a screw, which machine would you have?
   A. inclined plane   C. pulley
   B. lever   D. wedge

J 16. Which machine would you use to split wood?
   F. inclined plane   H. pulley
   G. lever   J. wedge

C 17. What is anything that changes the way work is done?
   A. force
   B. fulcrum
   C. machine
   D. motion

Answer Key   **(page 25 of 26)**   **Assessment Guide**   **AG 157**

Unit F

Name _____

__G__ 18. Which property of matter keeps it moving in a straight line?
    F. energy   **H.** magnetism
    G. inertia   **J.** mass

__B__ 19. What is produced by the kinetic energy of falling water?
    A. geothermal energy   **C.** chemical energy
    B. hydroelectric power   **D.** solar power

Write the answer to each question. 6 points each

20. What are three examples of simple machines? How do they make work easier?

    Possible answer: Simple machines, such as inclined planes, wedges, and pulleys, make work easier by changing the amount or direction of the force.

21. Suppose you plug in a string of electric lights. If the lights are in a series circuit, what happens if one light goes out? Why? What happens if a light goes out in a parallel circuit? Why?

    Possible answer: A series circuit has only one path for the current to follow. If one light goes out, all the lights go out.
    A parallel circuit has more than one path for the current to follow. If one light goes out, the other lights in the string will stay lit.

22. In a compound machine, two or more simple machines work together. Name two compound machines. Which simple machines make up each compound machine?

    Possible answers: A pair of scissors has levers and wedges.
    A knife is a lever and a wedge.

Name _____

23. Speed tells you how an object's position changes during a certain amount of time. Answer the questions in Part A and Part B to calculate the speed of certain objects.

Part A What do you need to measure to find an object's speed? What is the formula for finding the speed of an object?

    Possible answer: To find an object's speed, you need to measure distance and the time it takes the object to move the distance. The formula is speed = distance ÷ time.

Part B Suppose the Miller family, the Jones family, and the Edwards family are driving separately to meet at a favorite vacation place. Use the information below to determine the speed of each car. Complete the table. Remember to use the formula for finding speed and to show your work.

Family	Distance Traveled	Time Traveled	Speed
Miller	180 kilometers	3 hours	**60 km/hr**
Jones	300 kilometers	4 hours	**75 km/hr**
Edwards	210 kilometers	3 hours	**70 km/hr**

    Possible answer: I determined the speed of each car by using the formula speed = distance ÷ time. The speed of each car is as follows. Miller family: 180 km/3 hrs = 60 km/hr; Jones family: 300 km/4 hrs = 75 km/hr; Edwards family: 210 km/3 hrs = 70 km/hr.

© Harcourt

CURRICULUM